OXFORD *Playscripts*

Leon Garfield

adapted by Robert Staunton

Smith

TOWER HOUSE SCHOOL

Oxford University Press

Oxford University Press, Great Clarendon Street, Oxford OX2 6DP

Oxford New York
Athens Auckland Bangkok Bogotá Buenos Aires
Calcutta Cape Town Chennai Dar es Salaam Delhi
Florence Hong Kong Istanbul Karachi Kuala Lumpur
Madrid Melbourne Mexico City Mumbai Nairobi Paris
Sãu Paulo Singapore Taipei Tokyo Toronto Warsaw

and associated companies in
Berlin Ibadan

Oxford is a trade mark of Oxford University Press

This adaptation of *Smith* © Robert Staunton 1997
Originally published as a novel by Leon Garfield under the
title *Smith* © 1967. This adaptation is published under licence
from Mrs Vivien Garfield.
Activity section © Steve Barlow and Steve Skidmore 1997
First published 1997
Reprinted 1998

ISBN 0 19 831297 0

All applications to perform this adaptation of *Smith* should
be addressed in the first instance to the Permissions Controller,
Educational Division, Oxford University Press, Great Clarendon
Street, Oxford OX2 6DP.

All rights reserved. No part of this publication may be reproduced,
stored in a retrieval system, or transmitted, in any form or by any
means, without the prior permission in writing of Oxford University
Press. Within the UK, exceptions are allowed in respect of any fair
dealing for the purpose of research or private study, or criticism or
review, as permitted under the Copyright, Designs and Patents Act
1988 or in the case of reprographic reproduction in accordance with
the terms of licences issued by the Copyright Licensing Agency.
Enquiries concerning reproduction outside those terms and in other
countries should be sent to the Rights Department, Oxford University
Press, at the address above.

Printed and bound in the United Kingdom at the
University Press, Cambridge

The publishers would like to thank the following for permission to
reproduce photographs:
Mary Evans Picture Library: pp 112, 115, 117, 123; Museum of
London/John Roque's Map of London 1746: pp 108, 109

Illustrations are by Martin Cottam and Stefan Chabluk

Cover illustration by Simon Fell

Contents

Characters

In order of their appearance on stage:

Character	Description
Smith	*a twelve-year-old pickpocket*
Chorus 1 **Chorus 2** **Chorus 3**	*cloaked figures who comment on the action*
Mr Field	*an elderly gentleman murdered in Curtis Court*
Man in Brown 1 **Man in Brown 2**	*murderers of Mr Field*
Mr Black	*(not his real name); has a wooden leg*
A Well-dressed Lawyer	*who witnesses Mr Field's murder; (he must be played by the same actor as takes the part of Mr Billing)*
Miss Bridget	*Smith's sensible sister*
Miss Fanny	*Smith's emotional sister*
Landlord	*of the Red Lion Tavern*
Mr Jones	*a hangman at Newgate prison*
Prisoner 1 **Prisoner 2** **Prisoner 3**	*debtors at Newgate prison*
A Lawyer **A Clerk** **A Schoolmaster** **A Priest** **A Bookseller**	*Smith approaches these characters and asks them to teach him to read*
Lord Tom	*a highwayman, who dresses in green*
Mr Mansfield	*a blind magistrate*
Miss Mansfield	*the magistrate's daughter*
Footman 1 **Footman 2**	*Mr Mansfield's servants*
Meg	*a scullery maid in Mr Mansfield's house*

Mr Billing	*a lawyer*
Muffin Man	*delivering to Mr Mansfield's house*
Coachman	*(non-speaking)*
Prisoner 4	*an old man who befriends Smith at Newgate prison*
Dick Mulrone	*a condemned highwayman on his way to be hanged (non-speaking)*
Bob	*an innkeeper*
Charlie Parkin	*a constable*
Mrs Parkin	*his wife*
Andrews	*an elderly servant of Mr Field, at the house at Prickler's Hill*
Miss Field	*sister to Mr Field*
Mr Lennard	*Mr Field's lawyer*
A Sexton	*summoned to dig in the graveyard at Prickler's Hill for Mr Field's money*

The following scenes require extra non-speaking parts

Scene 1	*Crowd on the streets of London* *Group of clerks and lawyers*
Scene 5	*Crowd attending Dick Mulrone's hanging*
Scene 9	*Footmen to remove bodies*

A Note on the Set

The story of Smith is set in eighteenth-century England. The action of the playscript takes place in several locations: the streets and alleyways of London; the countryside beyond the city; the squalor of Newgate prison; inns and taverns frequented by highwaymen and murderers; the houses of the rich and the homes of the poor. The set needs to create these many locations, but also it must help the action of the play flow easily and swiftly between these different places.

The area towards the back of the stage should be raised at a number of different levels. It should create the appearance of an eighteenth-century London slum – dark streets, doorways into buildings and narrow alleyways offering characters in the play the opportunity for quick escapes and sudden entrances. This background setting should be lit dimly to create shadows and dark hiding places from where characters can witness the action unseen. The area could also be draped with dark, stained clothes, hanging like dirty washing, to complete the effect.

Two prongs of staging extending forwards towards the audience mark out three acting areas at a lower level than the background set. The use of steps will allow easy access to these lower performance spaces. Here, the set can be made up of boxes, sacking, barrels, planks, etc., in fact anything to add to the atmosphere created by the background setting. Essential props and small items of furniture can then be hidden amongst the clutter of the set.

In many cases, a specific location may be set between scenes during the blackout. As a general rule, the area stage left becomes the Mansfields' house, Mr Field's house at Prickler's Hill and Bob's Inn; the area centre stage is used for the London streets, Newgate prison and Finchley Common, and the area stage right as the cellar of the Red Lion Tavern, The Wrestler's Inn and the Parkins' cottage. At other times, the Chorus may move staging and/or furniture to create a particular place, and characters can use the rest of the performance areas – both back and front, high and low, as they feel appropriate.

An asterisk in the text indicates that a word or phrase appears in the Glossary on page 126.

A Note on the Chorus

The Chorus should be on stage for most of the play (they exit on page 86 for a brief period). When they are not directly involved in the action they should have places within the set where they can hide, but still watch what is going on. The Chorus are only visible to the audience and should be ignored by all the other characters in the playscript. However, on occasions, the Chorus provide Smith with ideas which come into his head. They also sometimes describe actions which the cast should act out.

Scene 1

Lights up on the streets of eighteenth-century London. ***Smith*** *enters wearing many layers of old, ill-fitting, hand-me-down clothes. The three cloaked figures of the* ***Chorus****, appear from amongst the set.*

Smith Smith! Twelve years old!

Chorus 1 Smith! He lives in a rough, tough time. Without parents. Without much at all!

Smith A pickpocket by trade.

Chorus 2 Well, he's got to earn a living – got to eat.

Chorus 3 There's the hanging if he gets caught. Hanging! And for trying to stay alive.

Smith Oh, it's all right for the rich with money and houses and things. They don't need to steal.

Chorus 1 Just to live in one of those big houses, with servants, horses and carriages, proper furniture. Clothes.

Smith Still – they've got it all, and us without 'as to try and take a bit from them.

Chorus 2 Carefully, mind! Oh, so very carefully.

Smith Smith! Twelve years old.

Chorus 1 *(Indicating Smith)* Now being that old is a marvel. Things like smallpox, consumption*, brain fever – even the hangman's rope have given Smith a wide berth.

Chorus 3 Probably think they'll catch something. Smith don't wash you see. Washing costs money.

Chorus 2 In truth, they're not quick enough to catch him.

Silently, a crowd of shrouded figures enters from the back of the stage. They stand waiting, trying to keep warm. The ***Chorus*** *mingle with the crowd.*

Chorus 1 A dingy, narrow street. December. Cold.

There is the sound of a moving carriage off stage. The carriage stops.

Chorus 2 Mr Field gets out of his carriage and stumps up Ludgate Hill.

Mr Field *enters. He is wearing a heavy coat. He stands looking around deciding on which direction to take.* ***Smith*** *hides behind one of the crowd.* ***Mr Field*** *begins to walk around the stage, between the crowd.* ***Smith*** *stalks him, waiting for an opportunity to rob him.*

Chorus 3 To judge by his complexion, a country gentleman.

Mr Field *continues to walk between the crowd;* ***Smith*** *follows him.*

Chorus 1 He seems to know where he's going. Deeper and deeper into the musty, tottering part of town, where Smith hunts fast and well. Godliman Street. Curtis Alley, Curtis Court – a quiet place, full of lawyers' offices.

Mr Field *stops. As he turns and looks behind him,* ***Smith*** *dodges to hide.*

Mr Field Brrr! Feels like someone's walked over my grave.

Mr Field *begins to walk again; Smith follows.* ***Mr Field*** *is now aware that someone is following him. He looks back several times, but each time* ***Smith*** *dodges out of sight.*

Mr Field Now, where did that boy go? This way? That way? Where is he?

Smith *brushes past Mr Field and moves in amongst the crowd.*

Mr Field *(Alarmed)* Careful lad. Watch where you are going!

Chorus 1 In an instant it is done. Smith brushes against the old fellow and empties his pocket. Neat.

The crowd exit very quietly; the ***Chorus*** *remain.* ***Mr Field*** *begins to check his pockets.*

Chorus 2 *(To Smith in a warning voice)* The sound of footsteps, coming this way!

Smith Footsteps! I'll be blocked in! Into the doorway!

The ***Chorus*** *and* ***Smith*** *hide amongst the set. From their hiding places, they watch the action which follows.* ***Mr Field*** *now realizes that he has been robbed.*

Mr Field Come back here, you little devil!

Two men, dressed in brown, enter. ***Man in Brown 2*** *hangs back to check whether there is anyone else in the alley.* ***Man in Brown 1*** *moves towards Mr Field.*

Man in Brown 1 *(To Mr Field)* A good day to you, sir.

Mr Field Good day.

Man in Brown 1 *gets very close to Mr Field and stabs him.* ***Mr Field*** *falls to the ground dead.* ***Man in Brown 1*** *then searches Mr Field's coat pockets, while* ***Man in Brown 2*** *keeps watch.*

Man in Brown 1 No! God rot the old fool!

He calls in a hushed voice to Man in Brown 2.

Man in Brown 1 He ain't got it!

Man in Brown 2 He must have! Hurry!

*Enter **Mr Black**. He walks with a limp and uses a walking stick.*

Mr Black *(To the men in brown)* Well?

Man in Brown 1 Nothing – nothing, your honour.

Mr Black Fool! Liar! Look again!

Man in Brown 2 He's told you – there's nothing!

Mr Black It must be there.

***Mr Black** approaches the body of Mr Field to search it for himself, but he is startled and horrified to recognize the dead man.*

Mr Black *(Surprised and angry)* But that's not Andrews!

***Mr Black** moves away from the body.*

Man in Brown 1 Well, it ain't here!

Man in Brown 2 If we stays much longer, we'll be on our way to joining him – at the end of a rope.

Mr Black It was supposed to be Andrews!

Man in Brown 2 *(Urgently)* Come on – there's someone coming!

*The two **men in brown** hurriedly bundle **Mr Black** off stage. The **Chorus** reappear.*

Chorus 1 Smith does not move.

Chorus 2 There are voices and clustering footsteps coming from the far side of the alley.

A crowd of clerks and lawyers enter moving slowly towards the body of Mr Field.

Chorus 3 Pale-faced clerks and thin-necked lawyers have caught the scent of spilt blood and come out of their chambers to congregate and stare.

__Smith__ comes out of his hiding place and quietly joins the crowd. They all stare down at the dead body.

Chorus 2 Smith silently joins the outskirts of the crowd, muttering away with the best of them.

Suddenly, __Smith__ runs away.

Chorus 1 Then he is through, like a needle through shoddy* to Godliman Street and beyond.

A __well-dressed lawyer__ enters. He is separate from the crowd and seems to be viewing the scene from a doorway.

Chorus 3 And as Smith leaves, a door opens in the court, and someone comes quietly out.

The __lawyer__ sees __Smith__ running away and watches him leave the stage. Then he exits. The crowd exit taking the body of Mr Field with them. The __Chorus__ remain on stage. __Smith__ enters running, clambering, and dodging around the stage.

Chorus 1 A quarter of a mile off, on the other side of St Paul's, Smith stops running, sits on the steps, and fumbles in his pocket.

__Smith__ sits down and takes a packet out of his pocket.

Smith What have I got this time? Something valuable! Something that is worth the old gentleman's life. (*He opens the package and is disappointed*) A document? A document! What use is that to me? I can't read! Not a word!

The __Chorus__ move close to Smith.

Chorus 1 A hundred stratagems present themselves to Smith – but he can't use them.

Smith *(Thinking out loud and putting on a learned voice)* I could apply to the various scholars of my acquaintance.

Chorus 2 But who can you trust?

Smith *(Thinking out loud)* I could cut the document into its lines, or even words – and give them each to a different reader.

Chorus 3 But what if you muddle the order, or even lose a few essential words?

Smith *(Thinking out loud)* Home to the Red Lion.

***Smith** exits. Blackout.*

. . . .

Scene 2

*Lights up. The area stage right is set as the cellar of the Red Lion Tavern. **Miss Bridget** and **Miss Fanny** are sitting on stools, sewing old clothes. The **Chorus** are on stage, watching the action, but partially hidden amongst the set. **Smith** enters from the back of the stage and makes his way towards the cellar steps. The **landlord** enters and grabs **Smith** by the scruff of his neck.*

Landlord Not strung up yet?

***Smith** does not answer.*

Landlord I spoke to you, Smith!

Smith Did you now, landlord! I thought it was a belch from the Old Ditch*.

Landlord You cheeky...

*He clips **Smith's** ear.*

Smith Ohh!

Landlord Got him that time!

*The **landlord** pushes **Smith** towards the cellar and exits. **Smith** tumbles down the steps into the cellar.*

Miss Bridget (*To Smith*) You asked for it. You brought it on yourself. The landlord has had enough of you.

Miss Fanny Poor little Smut! One day Bridget, he'll come down those cellar steps stone dead! *(To Smith)* You will you know, Smut!

Smith I'm not complaining. Saw an old gent done in today.

Miss Bridget Indeed! And what's that to do with abusing the landlord?

Smith Me mind was on other things.

Miss Bridget That's no excuse! Fanny and me brung you up to be genteel. We feels the disgrace.

Miss Fanny Put a dab of vinegar on your little lug*, Smut. It will take out the sting.

***Smith** takes out the document.*

Smith Look what I got this time!

Miss Fanny What is it?

Smith It was what he was done in for.

***Miss Bridget** takes the document from **Smith** and studies it. **Miss Fanny** moves so that she can see the document over her sister's shoulder.*

Miss Bridget It's a deed of property. That queer thing that looks so like a horse and cart is the word 'property'. Indeed it is. I'd know it anywhere.

Smith Why was he done in for it? Why was they so frantic when they couldn't find it? Poor old fool!

Miss Bridget Reasons, reasons.

Miss Fanny *(Looking over Miss Bridget's shoulder)* I think it's a confession or an accusation. For that's the sort of thing that murder's done for – excepting money; and it ain't money. Now – though I don't quarrel with Bridget's, 'property', for I believe her to be right, there's a 'whereas', most distinct; and that piece like a nest of maggots, there – I know to be 'felonious'. Oh yes indeed, Smut dear; you got a confession, which will be very valuable if we can only find out what's been done. For, if they was willing and able to kill for it – well, they'll be equal willing to pay for it! Clever Smut. So we must get it read out to us, so we know where to apply.

Miss Bridget And who, Miss Fanny, would you ask?

Smith *(Interrupting)* Lord Tom can read.

Miss Fanny Lord Tom, he's a scholar.

Miss Bridget That high toby* is so much in his cups, that his mouth's grown like a spout! Mark my words, miss, I'd as soon trust him with anything worth money as I would the landlord! Not that I think the paper's worth money at all: for it's neither more nor less than a deed of property.

Miss Bridget *moves away.* ***Smith,*** *thinking that she is going to take the document with her, snatches it back.*

Miss Bridget Sorry, Smut. Forgot I had it.

Miss Bridget *moves to a pile of clothes and begins sorting them.* ***Smith*** *makes as though to leave the cellar.*

Miss Fanny Where are you off to, Smut dear?

Smith Newgate, on business.

Miss Fanny What are you going to do with our document, Smut?

Smith Don't know yet.

Miss Fanny Wouldn't it be safer here?

Smith Why?

Miss Fanny Well, dear – if them that wanted it did in an old man for it, they wouldn't think twice about doing in a boy.

Smith Don't know I got it! Never saw me! There's only you and Miss Bridget here, what knows.

Miss Fanny Oh, yes... that's true. But you never can tell, Smut. Someone may have seen you. Won't you leave it behind?

Smith No.

Miss Fanny Are you going to show it to Lord Tom?

Smith Don't know. Maybe.

Miss Bridget Miss Fanny, if Smut's going to Newgate prison, tell him to screw some money out of that Mr Jones, the hangman – for there'll not be another stitch done on these dead men's clothes till there's some money on account! Hangmen is horrible customers!

Miss Fanny Mr Jones, Smut. See Mr Jones. Don't forget! Leave the document behind, Smut dear. It will be as safe as houses. I've a feeling you were seen and are in danger! I fear you'll be coming down those steps tonight stone dead!

Smith *leaves the cellar of the Red Lion Tavern, but remains on stage.* ***Miss Fanny*** *and* ***Miss Bridget*** *exit.*

Smith I'll learn to read. *(Looking at the document)* You and me's got business. *(Putting the document inside his layers of clothing)* You and me's going up in the world – just as soon as I gets you to talk. Off to Newgate prison!

Smith *walks towards Newgate prison, centre stage.* ***Mr Jones,*** *the hangman and three* ***prisoners*** *enter.* ***Prisoners 1*** *and* ***2***

sit or stand; ***Prisoner 3*** *paces up and down.* ***Mr Jones*** *keeps a watchful eye on them. The* ***Chorus*** *remain separate from the prisoners.*

Chorus 1 Newgate prison.

Chorus 2 Newgate prison is Smith's daily place of work. He runs errands for the prisoners. Two pence a dry mile and four pence when it rains.

Smith *approaches Mr Jones.*

Smith Morning, Mister Jones! Miss Bridget wants three shillings on account for her sewing.

Mr Jones Three shillings on account? You just watch your 'P's and 'Q's, my lad, otherwise you'll finish up being my customer and you'll pay then by a yardage of hemp* – the rope!

Mr Jones *gives* ***Smith*** *the three shillings.*

Smith 'P's and 'Q's, Mister Jones? Them's letters, ain't they? Show us a 'P', Mister Jones and then show us a 'Q' and I'll try to mind 'em!

Mr Jones You trying to be funny?

Mr Jones *hits Smith and exits.* ***Smith*** *looks towards the prisoners.*

Smith I only wanted two letters! Bleeding scholars! Want to keep everything for themselves. *(He indicates the prisoners)* Scholars all!

Chorus 3 Very educated people, debtors. You have to be educated to get into debt.

Smith *moves to Prisoner 1.*

Smith Learn me to read!

Prisoner 1 Not in a thousand years, my boy! Be happy that you can't. For what will you get by it? You'll read and fret over disasters that might never touch you. You'll read of bills overdue and creditors' anger – where you might have ignored it all for another month! Be advised, don't learn to read.

Smith *moves on to Prisoner 2.*

Smith Learn me to read, mister!

Prisoner 2 What do you want to learn to read for? No need for it. If it weren't for my skill as a reader, I'd not be here today. I was on the run, see – saw this sign – new goldsmith's shop. Stopped to read it – and they nicked me, so 'ere I am. No, stay away from reading and you'll stay away from trouble.

Smith *then approaches* ***Prisoner 3****, who is still pacing up and down.*

Smith Learn us to read!

Prisoner 3 *stops pacing and looks at Smith.*

Smith Oh, go on! Learn me to read, please!

Prisoner 3 Oh, all right then, Smith. It would be a pleasure. It would be a pleasure to learn you to read. Now the first thing you need to know about your reading is – come closer Smith. *(****Smith*** *leans close to Prisoner 3.)* This is how we begin our reading, Smith!

Prisoner 3 *seizes* ***Smith*** *by the nose and squeezes it hard.* ***Smith*** *yells in pain and runs away clutching his nose. The* ***prisoners*** *laugh and exit.*

Smith *(Speaking to himself)* I will learn to read.

Three citizens, a ***lawyer****, a* ***clerk*** *and a* ***schoolmaster*** *enter.*

Chorus 2 There are surely more scholars here, in the streets of London, than in Newgate prison?

Smith *(Calling out)* Learn me to read!

Lawyer A lawyer.

Clerk A clerk.

Schoolmaster A country schoolmaster.

All Three Learn you to read? No, never!

*They laugh and exit. **Smith** moves around the stage as if walking through the London streets.*

Chorus 3 A church.

*From the assorted clutter of the set, the **Chorus** place a box centre stage. Then they retreat and remain on the edge of the action. A **priest**, dressed in white, enters. He carries two silver candlesticks which he places on the box, and then exits.*

Chorus 2 Candlesticks!

Chorus 1 Very peaceful. No one around.

***Smith** approaches the church and does a double take as he notices the candlesticks. His fingers begin to itch.*

Chorus 3 Probably silver those candlesticks! Bit of weight in 'em. Those must be worth ...

*The **priest** enters carrying a Bible. He notices Smith.*

Priest What do you want, my child? What are you looking for?

Smith Er... guidance, Your Reverence?

Priest Are you lost?

Smith Oh no, your Worship. This is 'olborn 'ill! Learn me to read, your 'oliness. That's what I comes for. Learn me to read, so's I can read the 'oly Scriptures.

Priest If you come and stand by the door during Service, then you'll hear me reading from the Holy Scriptures, child. Won't that be a comfort and help to you?

Smith Oh yes, Your Grace. And I'm 'umbly obliged. But what of when I'm 'ome, all dirt and disorder? Who'll read to me then? And me two poor sisters – a-panting, a-groaning, a-supplicating for salvation? Who'll read to them? Oh no, Your Reverence – I got to learn to read, so's I can comfort myself in the dark o' the night and light a little lamp in me sisters' souls with perusing aloud from the good book.

Priest You're a little liar!

Smith And you're a fat bag of rotting flour. I 'ope the weevils* get you!

__Smith__ runs away. The __priest__, carrying the candlesticks and the Bible, chases Smith off stage. The __Chorus__ replace the priest's box. They then collect some books from the set and place them on the raised part of the stage. The __Chorus__ stand back but remain watching on the edge of the action.

Chorus 1 A bookshop.

A __bookseller__ enters carrying a pile of books. __Smith__ enters running. He sees the bookshop and stops running. He approaches the bookseller.

Smith Learn me to read, mister!

Bookseller Be off with you!

Smith Ain't you got no feeling for your trade? Don't you want it to prosper with more readers?

Bookseller I know you, you're a wicked little thief!

Smith Only because I'm ignorant.

Bookseller Get out of here.

__Smith__ climbs and moves towards the books on the raised part of the stage.

Smith Why won't you learn me?

Bookseller Keep your thieving hands to yourself!

Smith Why won't nobody learn me to read?

Bookseller Because they've too much sense, that's why. Now come down immediately and be careful.

Smith *(Stretching towards the books)* All this goodness and wisdom and learning.

Bookseller Touch a book and I'll finish you!

__Smith__ reaches for the books, which fall over. __Smith__ also falls, knocking over the __bookseller__.

Smith Too late! Gawd! Must've squashed flatter than an old sixpence!

__Smith__ gets up and hides. The __bookseller__ splutters, gets up, and starts to pick up the fallen books. Two __men in brown__ enter. One of them grabs the __bookseller's__ arm and whispers in his ear. The __bookseller__ nods in agreement.

Man in Brown 1 What was his name?

Bookseller They call him Smith.

Man in Brown 2 And where does he come from?

Bookseller Somewhere near the Ditch. I fancy it's the Red Lion Tavern.

Man in Brown 1 Got 'im.

*The two **men in brown** exit. The **bookseller** continues to pick up the fallen books.*

Bookseller Histories, memoirs, diaries, lexicons, grammars, atlases, journals, biographies, poems, plays. What a mess! I don't know why I bother, I really don't. A man of culture, of education like me reduced to tidying books. Just a minute, has that little beast stolen – Smith. Thief! Where has that thief got to!

*The **bookseller** exits. Blackout.*

Scene 3

*Lights up. The area stage right is set as the cellar of the Red Lion Tavern. **Miss Bridget** and **Miss Fanny** are sitting on stools, sewing clothes. **Lord Tom**, a highwayman, is talking in a friendly fashion to the two ladies. The **Chorus** can be seen amongst the set. The area stage left is now Mr Mansfield's house. At the lower level is a table set for supper and two chairs. On the raised area behind there is a bed made with clean sheets.*

Landlord *(Off stage)* Hello, Smith! Not nubbed* yet?

***Smith** enters from the back of the stage and walks towards the cellar steps. **Lord Tom** hears **Smith** approaching, nudges **Miss Fanny** and puts a finger to his lips. She smiles, joining in the conspiracy to trick Smith. **Lord Tom** takes out his pistol and creeps into a hiding place. Now, only the point of his pistol is visible. **Smith** starts down the cellar steps. He sees the pistol and freezes.*

Lord Tom Stand and deliver!

__Smith__ starts, misses his footing, and falls down the remaining steps into the cellar.

Smith I know the voice! It's Lord Tom.

__Lord Tom__ comes out of his hiding place. __Smith__ gets up.

Smith Pleased to see you, Lord Tom.

Chorus 1 Lord Tom, the highwayman, a dangerous, glittering, murdering adventurer of a gentleman in green.

Miss Fanny Do watch how you go, Smut, or you'll be coming down them steps stone dead! And then where will our document be?

Miss Bridget Did you see that degrading Mr Jones? For if you didn't, you can go straight out again.

Smith Here you are, Bridget! Three shillings from Mr Jones at Newgate.

__Smith__ gives __Miss Bridget__ the money.

Smith *(To Lord Tom)* They told me you was nubbed – but I never believed 'em.

Lord Tom Ah! *(Putting away his pistol)* It happens to all of us, sooner or later, Smut. With some, it's sooner, but with Lord Tom, let's hope it'll be vastly the later!

Miss Fanny *(Gratefully)* And so say all of us.

Smith Trade been good these past ten days?

Lord Tom Been on the Finchley Common, Smut, me young friend. Wild and free on the snaffling lay*.

Miss Bridget If by snaffling lay you mean pilfering from unarmed travellers, then say so. Or are you ashamed?

Smith Many coaches, Lord Tom? And was there danger?

Lord Tom Fine, smart carriages, little Smut! Windows fair sparkling with satin and brilliants. Like travelling stars, I tell you. Gleaming in the foggy nights! Stern with the gentry; courteous with the ladies. 'Madam, your necklace – if you please! Sir, your purse – or I'll blow your head off'.

Smith And did you? Did you blow any heads off this time, Lord Tom?

Lord Tom Only a pair of coachmen's, Smut! And then unwillingly – for they went for their weapons.

Smith How many coaches did you take?

Lord Tom Six, me friend! Six...

Miss Bridget Then where's your profit, you ugly murderer! Where's the necklaces and purses, sir?

Lord Tom Spent, Miss Bridget – as well you know. That's the way of our lives. Risk all for the chase – then spend the profit. The chase and the danger's all. There was a diamond brooch I parted with for an evening's ale in Highgate, ma'am. And, by God, but it was a good exchange! Eat, drink and be merry, as they say – for tomorrow we'll all be nubbed!

Miss Bridget A pity it wasn't yesterday.

Lord Tom *(To Smith)* But what's this I hear? The news I hear is that you've come upon a rare treasure, me lad! Already me rival in accomplishment? Well, indeed – I'm proud of you! A document, I hear tell. And curiously valuable – from all accounts.

Miss Fanny I told Lord Tom. And we're of an opinion that...

Miss Bridget *(Interrupting)* 'Tis nothing of value. A property deed most likely. Of no use to anyone at all.

Miss Fanny And I say it's a confession, Brid! Really, Lord Tom, dear – I'm convinced! Indeed the more I think on it, it had such – such a guilty look.

Lord Tom Well, then, let's put an end to this guessing and see it. Here, Smut, old comrade in arms, let's see the document. Lord Tom'll read it for you. Well, Smut, friend – where's the treasure?

***Smith** does not answer.*

Miss Bridget Not with one of those creeping debtors? How I hate debtors! They're worse than thieves!

Miss Fanny Then who's got it, Smut dear? Who's got our valuable document?

Smith The parson at St Andrew's.

Miss Bridget And who is he, when he's at home? You little liar!

Smith A friend o' mine.

Miss Bridget You made him up!

Smith No, Miss Bridget! True as I live and breathe. Big fat man all in white. Friend of mine. Cross my heart and hope to be nubbed.

Miss Bridget And where did you meet him?

Smith In church...

Miss Bridget Now I know you're lying. For you never was in church in all your born days. Liar and blasphemer! Oh, how I hate a liar! You come here, you young person – and I'll wash your mouth out with vinegar for you. Don't think you'll escape this time!

***Miss Bridget** gets up and advances on **Smith**, who dodges expertly behind Lord Tom.*

Lord Tom *(Moving away from Smith)* Never come 'tween a family.

***Smith** dodges behind Miss Fanny.*

Miss Fanny Poor Smut!

__Miss Fanny__ moves away from Smith. __Miss Bridget__ makes several dives at __Smith__ who puts anything between himself and his sister's grasp.

Miss Bridget I'll teach you to lie to me!

__Smith__ lunges towards the cellar exit. __Miss Fanny__ and __Lord Tom__ move to guard it, thereby blocking Smith's escape route.

Smith *(To Miss Fanny and Lord Tom)* Let me through!

Lord Tom Not till you give up the document.

Miss Fanny Oh, do as Lord Tom says, dear Smut, before Brid smashes you stone dead! For she is vexed.

__Miss Bridget__ continues to chase __Smith__, making grabs for his hair.

Miss Bridget Nothing'll save you this time! You little liar, you!

The __landlord__ appears in the cellar entrance.

Landlord *(Calling down)* Smith! Smith!

__Miss Bridget__ stops chasing __Smith__.

Landlord Forgot to tell you something.

Smith What, landlord?

Landlord You 'ad callers.

Smith Who? Me?

Landlord Yes, indeed. Had you off to a 'T'. Dirty, weaselish, villainous-looking remnant. Eyes like chips of coal. Teeth like the same. About twelve year old – 'That's him,' I says directly – 'Good!' says they. 'And where is he?' – 'Nubbed, most likely,' says I – 'Oh no!' says they, 'we'll be back then – to inspect the remains.' Then they was off. No message. Just that!

Smith *(Anxiously)* What were they like?

Landlord They were wearing brown.

The ***landlord*** *exits.*

Smith It's them! They've come to slit my throat.

Lord Tom Don't you worry, me lad! There's no one who'd dare come here when he knows Lord Tom's on your side! By God, Smut! If they so much as set foot in here, I'll blow daylight through them! You've got a man to protect you now. And I can't say fairer than that.

Smith You don't know 'em. They're not your sort, Lord Tom...

Miss Fanny Why, Smut, you'll be safe with Lord Tom! There, dear – you just give him our document and all will be well.

Smith You don't understand! They'll do for me any ways. They're that sort.

Miss Bridget *(Troubled)* Then what will you do?

Smith I don't know, but I can't stay here. Not now. Not at night. I'll go somewhere. Maybe to...

Lord Tom The parson at St Andrews?

Smith *(Defiantly)* Maybe.

Miss Bridget Don't lie now, child. It may be for the last time, and you'd go to hell.

Smith I got to go! For Gawd's sake, let me pass.

Lord Tom I'd protect you, Smut. Honest I would.

Miss Fanny The document, Smut. Won't you leave it, dear? It'll bring you no good...

Smith No! Never! Never! Besides, it's with the parson at St Andrew's.

Miss Fanny Oh, Smut, Brid's right and you're a liar, for you've got the document; it's inside your coat. I can see it, dear!

Smith Out 'o my way!

Two ***men in brown*** *enter. They remain in the shadows at the top of the cellar steps. In the cellar,* ***Smith****, with a desperate rush, pushes by* ***Lord Tom****,* ***Miss Fanny****, and* ***Miss Bridget****, and runs up the steps and across the stage.*

Chorus 2 From a doorway, two men dressed in brown, see Smith hurry out of the Red Lion Tavern.

Lord Tom*,* ***Miss Bridget****, and* ***Miss Fanny*** *follow Smith up the steps.*

Lord Tom We'll not catch him, not in these streets and alleys. He'll be back!

Lord Tom*,* ***Miss Fanny****, and* ***Miss Bridget*** *exit. The two* ***men in brown*** *follow* ***Smith****, who is aware of being followed.* ***Smith*** *disappears into the background set followed by the* ***men in brown****.*

Chorus 1 The two men in brown set off in the wake of the hurrying boy. Portpool Lane; Hatton Gardens; Chart Street; back to Saffron Hill; then Holborn Hill; Union Court; Hatton Gardens again; and then to Cross Street; Saffron Hill; Cox's Court.

Smith *reappears followed closely by the* ***men in brown****. He dashes about the stage, hiding in the recesses, checking that he is losing the men in brown, weaving, as though running down narrow lanes, and finally he hides. The two* ***men in brown*** *are exhausted by their efforts to catch Smith.*

Man in Brown 1 *(Breathless)* Fer God's sake! I can't go another step! Me heart'll burst – I swear it!

Man in Brown 2 All right! We'll go back – some'ow – to the Red Lion. We'll wait there! *(Pause)* God rot the crafty little perisher!

*The two **men in brown** exit. Slowly and carefully **Smith** comes out of his hiding place.*

Smith *(Triumphantly)* That's run them into the ground.

*From the layers of his clothing, **Smith** brings out a bottle of gin, and takes several very deep swigs. He drinks so much gin that it makes him retch.*

Chorus 3 Not a night to be out in: black, windy and cold.

***Smith**, affected by the gin, staggers a little as he crosses the stage. Unseen by Smith, **Mr Mansfield** enters. He is blind. He wears a heavy coat, a hat, smoked spectacles* and carries a stick. He moves cautiously as he is uncertain of his whereabouts. **Smith**, starting to run, collides with **Mr Mansfield** and they both fall in a heap. Mr Mansfield's spectacles, hat, and stick fall to the floor. **Mr Mansfield** reaches out and holds **Smith** by the ankle.*

Mr Mansfield Damn you, no! Help me, first. Help me! For pity's sake. Can't you see that I'm blind.

Smith If you let go of my ankle I'll help you up; that's if you are really blind.

Smith *pulls faces at Mr Mansfield.*

Smith Can you see me? What am I doing now?

Mr Mansfield I don't know! I swear I'm blind. Look at my eyes. Any light in 'em? Look for my smoked spectacles. They're somewhere about.

Smith *waves his arms grotesquely in front of Mr Mansfield.*

Smith What am I doing now?

Mr Mansfield *releases Smith's ankle, gets to his knees and searches the ground for his spectacles, hat, and stick.* ***Smith*** *gets out the document and waves it about.*

Smith What have I got in my hand?

Mr Mansfield My life, my boy... my life's in your hand.

Smith *puts the document in his pocket, takes* ***Mr Mansfield's*** *arm and helps him to his feet.*

Smith Here you are Mister Mole-in-the-hole. Here's me 'and, then up with you. Up on yer pins! And 'ere's your 'at and stick and black spectacles...though why you wear them foxes me!

Mr Mansfield Thank you, boy. Now – tell me if I'm in the street or the alley and I'll give you a guinea* for your pains.

Smith You're on the corner.

Mr Mansfield Facing which way?

Smith The Lord knows! I've been ill myself.

Mr Mansfield Fever?

Smith Half a pint o' gin.

Smith *takes* ***Mr Mansfield's*** *hand and shakes it.*

Smith Smith. Smith: 'unted, 'ounded, 'omeless and part gin sodden. Smith: twelve years old. That's me! Very small, but wiry, as they say. Dark 'aired and lately residing in the Red Lion Tavern off Saffron 'ill. Smith.

Mr Mansfield Mansfield. Blind as a wall for these past twelve years. Well-to-do, but not much enjoying it. Mansfield. Residing at number seven Vine Street, under the care of a daughter. Mansfield. Believe it or not – a magistrate!

Smith *(Dropping Mr Mansfield's hand)* Gawd! 'oo'd 'ave thought I'd ever be shaking hands with a bleeding Justice?

Mr Mansfield Just point me towards the church that should stand at one end of the street and the guinea's yours, Smith, with my deepest thanks.

Smith It seems a lot for a little.

Smith *turns* ***Mr Mansfield*** *to face the right direction.*

Mr Mansfield Thank you, Smith.

Mr Mansfield *offers* ***Smith*** *the guinea which he takes.*

Smith Thank *you*, Mister Mansfield.

Mr Mansfield Goodnight to you, Smith!

Smith Same to you, Mister Mansfield, Justice of the Peace.

Smith *watches as Mr Mansfield taps his way awkwardly down the street.* ***Mr Mansfield*** *stumbles.* ***Smith*** *can see that he needs help in finding his way.*

Chorus 1 *(To Smith)* Poor old gent.

Chorus 2 These streets on a dark night are no place for a blind man.

Chorus 3 Remember what happened in Curtis Alley? Murder!

*After a moment or two of indecision **Smith** walks over to assist Mr Mansfield.*

Mr Mansfield Smith? Is that you, Smith? Didn't expect you...

Smith Going the same way myself.

Mr Mansfield To Vine Street?

Smith Thereabouts.

Mr Mansfield Glad to hear it, Smith.

Smith Oh well – 'ere's me 'and, then... you old blind Justice, you! Just tell me where to turn and where to cross and I'll see you 'ome safe and sound. After all – I ain't done much for that guinea.

***Smith** takes hold of **Mr Mansfield's** hand and they set off for Vine Street. The journey takes them around the stage as many times as is necessary. They talk as they walk.*

Smith Was it a sickness?

Mr Mansfield My blindness, you mean? No, lost my sight when a house burned down. Lost my wife as well. A costly fire, that!

Smith Oh.

Mr Mansfield Take the next turning on the left, Smith.

Smith What's it like – being blind?

Mr Mansfield Dark, Smith. Very dark. What's it like having eyes?

Smith The moon's gone in again – so we're two of a kind, Mister Mansfield, you an' me.

Mr Mansfield Vine Street is the next street that crosses this one. My house is to the right. I'll be safe enough now, Smith.

Smith No trouble. I'm going the same way. To the door, Mister Mansfield.

Mr Mansfield If you've nothing better to do, will you come in and take a bite of late supper with my daughter and me, Smith?

Smith Don't mind if I do, Mister Mansfield.

Mr Mansfield Stay the night, Smith, if you wish. It is late and very unpleasant.

Smith I don't mind if I do, Mister Mansfield.

Mr Mansfield Any family, Smith?

Smith Sisters. Two of 'em.

Mr Mansfield Likely to worry?

Smith Not much.

Mr Mansfield As long as we get a message to them, that's it settled?

Smith Just as you say, Mister Mansfield.

Mr Mansfield Anything else I can do for you, Smith?

__Smith__ takes the document from his pocket, looks at Mr Mansfield, then puts it back again. __Miss Mansfield__ enters and makes her way to Mr Mansfield's house, stage left. She looks out along the street. It is clear that she has been waiting anxiously for her father's return.

Smith No, thank you, Mister Mansfield. You done all you can. Number seven, Vine Street.

__Mr Mansfield__ and __Smith__ approach the house. __Miss Mansfield__ recognizes her father.

TOWER HOUSE SCHOOL

Chorus 2 Miss Mansfield sees her father with Smith who seems to be the filthiest, wretchedest, and most sinister looking object in the town.

Miss Mansfield Papa! I was so worried! You've been gone so long, sir. I thought you was lost!

Mr Mansfield Daughter, this is Smith. As good-hearted a child as the town can boast of.

Miss Mansfield *(Looking at Smith with dislike, but in a gentle voice)* Pleased to make your acquaintance, Smith. Any friend of my father's is more than welcome.

***Miss Mansfield** takes her father's arm. She then takes his coat and hat from him.*

Chorus 1 Miss Mansfield's face does not show any friendliness. In fact her face very clearly says, 'So you deceived my father! Very well, then. You won't deceive me! I've a pair of eyes in my head!'

Mr Mansfield Daughter, Smith will be taking supper with us, and then he'll stay the night. For it's very bitter in the air and he's far from home.

Miss Mansfield Any friend of yours, sir, is more than welcome.

Chorus 3 After years of looking after her father, Miss Mansfield is very accustomed to being able to show her feelings physically, safe in the knowledge that he cannot see them.

Chorus 2 She scowls and grimaces and sometimes even shakes her small fist when the old man's disability causes her annoyance – which it often does!

***Miss Mansfield** guides her father to a chair by the table, where he sits down. All the time her face shows the irritation she has for her father's behaviour. She then exits with her father's coat, and hat.*

Mr Mansfield Sit down, Smith, and eat.

__Smith__ sits down at the table.

Mr Mansfield My daughter's a saint. And you don't meet a saint every day, Smith.

Smith No, you don't.

__Smith__ and __Mr Mansfield__ eat their supper.

Chorus 3 Smith talks to Mr Mansfield about life in the streets of the town, life in the Red Lion Tavern's cellar, life in Newgate prison, of death by hanging at Tyburn* and death in – Curtis Court.

Mr Mansfield Indeed, I heard of the murder that took place in Curtis Court of a well-known and wealthy gentleman.

Smith Poor old so-and-so.

Mr Mansfield Did you see him, then?

Smith No, I never saw 'im, but I heard about it. Poor old so-and-so.

Mr Mansfield His name was Mr Field. He lived at Prickler's Hill in Hertfordshire. I knew him. I wish I had his killer before me.

Smith So do I, Mister Mansfield. Why was 'e done in?

Mr Mansfield Oh, who knows, Smith. Some vile, dark business no doubt. You know it troubles me.

Smith What troubles you, Mister Mansfield?

Mr Mansfield My blindness. Because I shall never clap eyes on the murderer. Because, till the day I die I shall never know what such a monster looks like. D'you understand me, Smith? To me angels and devils are all the same thing.

__Miss Mansfield__ enters.

Miss Mansfield It's very late for this young man to still be up talking. He looks tired, sir! His bed is ready and he ought to be in it.

Mr Mansfield Yes, I suppose you are right. Well, good night then, Smith. Sleep well, boy.

__Miss Mansfield__ helps __Mr Mansfield__ up from his chair and they both exit. __Smith__ moves to the bed and stands looking at it.

Chorus 1 Though Smith has slept on straw all his life, he isn't so ignorant as not to know a bed when he sees one.

__Smith__ prods the bed, sits on it, lies on it and finally, fully clothed, gets in it.

Smith So comfortable, so soft, and so warm.

Chorus 2 Smith grins and falls directly to sleep.

Chorus 3 He sleeps without dreaming, without even moving.

Blackout.

• •

Scene 4

Lights up. In Mr Mansfield's house, stage left, __Smith__ is asleep in his bed on the raised area. The supper table from the previous scene is now the desk in Mr Mansfield's study. There are books and papers on top of it. The area centre stage is set with a tin bath, large sheet, a sulphur ladle, a scrubbing brush, and a coal scuttle. A nervous __Miss Mansfield__ enters and approaches the bed. She is carrying her father's stick in her hand. She is careful to avoid close contact with Smith for he is both dirty and possibly dangerous. The __Chorus__ are visible.

Miss Mansfield Smith! Boy! Wake up! Directly!

She pokes him with the stick.

Chorus 1 Smith wakes and seeing only Miss Mansfield's furious concern, and the stick, rolls swiftly away.

__Smith__ falls out of bed, onto the floor and swears. He then rolls under the bed.

Chorus 2 He has forgotten that he is sleeping two feet off the floor.

Miss Mansfield *(Outraged)* Language!

Again __Miss Mansfield__ pokes at Smith with the stick. __Smith__ remains under the bed trying to avoid the stick.

Mr Mansfield *(From off stage)* Is there something wrong up there? What's wrong?

Miss Mansfield Nothing, Papa! *(She laughs)* Your young friend fell out of bed! No harm done. *(She mutters at Smith)* Come out! (*She prods him with her stick*) No one's going to harm you!

__Mr Mansfield__ enters and approaches his daughter.

Mr Mansfield Are you there, daughter? What is going on?

Miss Mansfield Papa! You shouldn't have come up without help! You might have fallen, sir!

Mr Mansfield Mornin', Smith. Sleep well? My daughter has a fine breakfast for you. She's a saint, child! As I told you, a real saint!

Smith *(From under the bed)* Mornin', Mister Mansfield.

Mr Mansfield What, still in bed? The voice betrays you! Give me your hand.

__Miss Mansfield__ crouches down and mouthes to Smith to come out.

Chorus 1 As she bends to Smith, her lips move to say, 'Please, come out!'

Mr Mansfield Where's your hand, Smith?

Chorus 2 Miss Mansfield's eyes fill with tears. As though saying to Smith, 'I beg you – for pity's sake, boy! Don't shame me in his blind eyes!'

Smith *comes out from under the bed.* ***Miss Mansfield*** *stands up.* ***Smith*** *offers his hand to Mr Mansfield.*

Smith Here's me hand, then... you old blind Justice, you!

Mr Mansfield And after breakfast will you go back to your cellar, Smith?

Smith *shrugs his shoulders.*

Miss Mansfield *(In a careless, every day tone)* Smith, Mr Mansfield means, will you stay here? And work for your board and keep, of course! Mr Mansfield is very concerned about you. He thinks you deserve better of the world than you've got, and would give it to you. My father is quite a saint, you know...

Mr Mansfield Come, daughter! 'Tis your own idea.

Miss Mansfield Never! Never in ten thousand years! I read it all in your face, sir.

Mr Mansfield My face?

Miss Mansfield 'Tis like an open book to me.

Chorus 3 Which ever one of them suggested the idea, Smith has no intention of staying in the house in Vine Street.

Miss Mansfield *(Giving her father an irritated look)* That's settled then. Mr Mansfield will employ you in the stables, Smith... *(She looks heavenward as though saying 'God help me')* and I will attend to your improvement. For a beginning, Smith, I shall teach you to read.

Smith *beams with delight at the prospect of being able to read.*

Miss Mansfield I think he's pleased, Papa. I suppose he's fond of horses.

Mr Mansfield We will send a servant to the Red Lion Tavern, to inform your sisters of the arrangement.

Smith No, sir. I'll go. I'll tell them myself. I can go, tomorrow.

Mr Mansfield As you wish, Smith. You will know them better than we do.

***Mr** and **Miss Mansfield** exit. **Smith** takes the document from his clothes and speaks to it.*

Smith Won't be long now, old fellow! Soon you and me will be better acquainted. And then – up we'll go in the world.

There is the sound of approaching footsteps.

Smith Footsteps!

***Smith** looks around in panic to find somewhere to hide his precious document. From his layers of clothing, he takes out a dirty handkerchief, wraps the document in it, and hides it quickly among the bed clothes. Two **footmen** enter, and approach Smith.*

Footman 1 Up with you.

Footman 2 And then down with you.

Smith What do you mean?

Footman 1 Miss's instructions. She says, afore you commence on scrubbing the yard, that self same necessary thing must be done to you. So, down to the scullery, young Smith.

***Smith** looks around for a way to escape.*

Footman 2 To the scullery, young Smith.

*The **footmen** take hold of **Smith** and half-drag him towards the tin bath, centre stage. **Meg**, the scullery maid, enters, removes the dirty bed clothes from the bed, and then exits.*

Footman 1 I don't suppose you recall ever having been washed, and consequently suspect that the task will be long, hard, and painful. You are not mistaken.

__Smith__ makes several attempts to escape before they reach the bath.

Footman 2 Take off them wretched rags, Smith.

Smith Rags? What rags?

Footman 1 Your clothes, Smith. Take off your clothes.

Footman 2 The windows are barred and the door shut, Smith!

__Chorus 1__ and __2__ step forward, pick up the sheet, and hold it in front of the bath. Behind the sheet, __Smith__ undresses slowly, taking off layer after layer of clothing. The __footmen__ stare in amazement.

Smith Ain't you never seen a person take off his clothes before?

Impatient to get the job done, the __footmen__ grab at __Smith__ to speed up his undressing.

Smith 'Ave the goodness to wait till I'm done, gen'lemen! 'Ave the goodness!

__Smith__ gets into the bath.

Smith *(Suspiciously)* Ready.

Chorus 1 One of the footmen doses the bath with sulphur to clean Smith of the fleas that live on his body. Then he takes a ladle, to spoon off the livestock as it rushes to the surface. The other sets about scrubbing Smith.

One of the __footmen__ picks up the ladle and 'spoons off the fleas from the water'. The other picks up a scrubbing brush and sets to work on Smith. __Smith__ cries out loudly during his ordeal.

Chorus 2 With the job done, Smith is taken out of the bath, rinsed, and wrapped in a sheet.

*The **footmen** take the sheet from **Chorus 1** and **2** and wrap it round **Smith**. Finally the **footmen** gather up Smith's dirty clothes and put them in a coal scuttle. The **Chorus** retreat from the action.*

Smith Me clothes. Me belongings. I can't go about like this.

Footman 2 A livery* is being cut down for you to wear.

Footman 1 You'll have to wait a little while for your new clothes, so back to your room.

*The **footmen** exit with the coal scuttle. **Smith** walks towards his bed wrapped in the sheet. On reaching the bed, **Smith** is horrified to find it bare.*

Smith The bedding! It's gone! The document!

***Smith** sits on the bed, with his head sunk onto his chest, totally depressed. The two **footmen** enter carrying Smith's new livery which is blue with brass buttons.*

Footman 1 Your new clothing, Smith.

***Smith** just stares into space.*

Footman 2 Would you like to try it on?

Footman 1 What is the matter with you, boy?

Footman 2 He's still in shock from being washed, I suppose.

Footman 1 Are you ill? What's the matter with you?

Smith Nothing.

Footman 1 Let's leave him. You wait, in half an hour he'll be proudly trying on his new clothes and strutting around like a king of the weasles!

***Smith** continues to sit in the same position.*

Footman 2 Maybe he's taken a chill?

Footman 1 We'll ask in the kitchen what's to be done.

*As the two **footmen** exit, **Miss Mansfield** enters. They whisper to her.*

Footman 1 He ain't flushed or feverish, miss.

***Miss Mansfield** approaches Smith. The **footmen** remain on stage.*

Miss Mansfield *(Scowling)* Are you ill, Smith?

***Smith** does not reply.*

Miss Mansfield What's wrong with you?

*Still, **Smith** does not reply.*

Miss Mansfield Answer me!

Smith Nothing, miss. Nothing.

Miss Mansfield *(To the footmen)* Have the housekeeper arrange to have a drink brought to Smith.

***Miss Mansfield** and the two **footmen** exit.*

Smith I was so close and now it's gone! I don't know what to do.

*The **Chorus** move forward.*

Chorus 1 Several times during the day Miss Mansfield returns to see if Smith has recovered. But each time he seems more sunk in himself – as if something has perished inside, and all is sinking in for lack of support.

Chorus 2 She seeks the opinion of the housekeeper, who says that the boy has been poisoned by the sulphur in the bath and needs a special drink. But it is no use, Smith will not drink it.

Chorus 3 It was as though Smith had made up his mind to die.

***Smith** continues to sit with his head sunk on his chest. The **Chorus** move and hide amongst the set. **Meg** enters carrying blankets and a tankard of ale. She puts the blankets down and speaks to Smith.*

Meg Come on, little one. It'll do you a power of good. Drink it up – for not the Red Lion itself has better ale. Nothing but kindness is meant. All's for your own good! They'll feed you an' clothe you and treat you like a human being. You'll want for naught here. They 'ad to wash you! You was filthy! You should have seen the sheets...

***Smith** raises his head.*

Smith The sheets? Did you see them?

***Smith's** eyes light up and his nose twitches.*

Meg Why, bless you, yes! They was that horrible, miss wanted 'em burned.

Smith And – did you?

Meg Lor' no! Burn good sheets? I boiled 'em!

Smith W-was there anything – anything else w-with the sheets?

Meg There was a handkerchief ... but 'twas far gone, I burned it...

Smith Burned it!

Meg I 'ad to! It was in a shameful state. It smelled dear, like ...well, I don't know what it smelled like, for I've nothing to compare it with. Powerful! Clinging! I only 'ope it'll wear off the master's paper...

Smith Paper? What – paper?

Meg Why – one of the master's documents that had somehow got itself muddled up in that dreadful 'andkerchief. Sometimes he drops 'is papers in the queerest places – what with his disability.

Smith What was in it?

Meg Lor' child! I don't know: 'twas a lawyer's document of sorts – and no one must read them save the mistress or the master's clerk. And then only when the master asks!

Smith Then how do you know it was a lawyer's document?

Meg 'Twas marked for the lawyers, Billing and Lennard, with 'oom we have dealings. Billing and Cooing I call 'em on account of Mr Billing being sweet on Miss Mansfield. He's in the parlour now. Such a handsome pair! So what else could it have been but one of the master's documents? Answer me that!

Smith Did – you give it to 'im?

Meg To our Mr Billing? Lor' no! That's for the master to do! Besides, it were for the other one, for Mr Lennard.

Smith So you g-gave it to Mister Mansfield?

Meg Questions, questions! Was you a cat, you'd be stone dead! No, I never gave it to him. There. I put it in his study along with his other papers. Only I put it at the bottom of the pile, so's the smell might wear off afore he comes to it.

***Meg** hands **Smith** the tankard.*

Meg Drink up your ale!

***Smith** drinks the ale.*

Meg Good! Just 'omesick, weren't you. Knew it all the time. Trust Meg!

***Meg** exits. **Smith** puts down the tankard, gets up, takes off the sheet, and puts on his livery.*

Smith I shall 'ave to look for it, that's all there is for it. The 'ouse seems to have gone quiet, so it's off to find Mister Mansfield's study and the document.

__Smith__ starts to look for Mr Mansfield's study. Just as he is about to go into it, __Miss Mansfield__ and __Mr Billing__ enter. __Smith__ quickly moves into the study and hides.

Mr Billing Goodnight to you, Miss Mansfield. A delightful evening.

Miss Mansfield Goodnight to you, Mr Billing.

Mr Billing I can see my way out, it is late and the night air is chilly.

Miss Mansfield I shall expect to see you again, soon, Mr Billing.

__Mr Billing__ bows respectfully and exits.

Miss Mansfield *(Speaking to herself)* At last, he's gone. Why did he have to stay so long this evening. Could he not see I was agitated? Poor Smith lies dying! I couldn't tell father. I'll have to sneak in a physician if the boy lasts till tomorrow. Maybe he is just worn out. I'll take a little peek. Just to see, otherwise I shall be awake all night with worry.

__Miss Mansfield__ moves to Smith's bed and finds that he is no longer there. __Smith__ comes out of his hiding place and begins sifting through the papers on the top of Mr Mansfield's desk.

Smith *(Quietly to himself)* Come on document! Where are you? Which one are you? So many – looking all the same!

Miss Mansfield *(Distraught)* He's gone! He knew he was dying and has struggled from his bed and crept away from the house, like an animal.

__Miss Mansfield__ moves away from the bed. Then she hears the rustle of papers from Mr Mansfield's study. She advances slowly and quietly towards the study.

Miss Mansfield Smith!

Smith *(Starting)* Gawd, I'm done for!

Miss Mansfield Is this how you repay Mr Mansfield? By robbing him? Stealing from a blind man! Is this the kindness of heart that so moved him? Nothing but the cunning skill of a cruel rogue.

Smith I ain't cruel. Really I ain't...

Miss Mansfield Smith, I'm disappointed, it's true. If it were up to me, I would have you clapped straight into Newgate. But you are more fortunate that Mr Mansfield is more understanding than I am. He never expected an angel out of you all at once. Go back to bed this instant – and we'll say no more of tonight. Don't gape. Don't try crying! Tears won't move me. Or don't you understand, Smith? You've been given another chance.

Blackout.

Scene 5

Lights up. ***Smith*** *is sweeping the yard at Mr Mansfield's house, centre stage. The* ***Chorus*** *are watching him, and listening. The area, stage left, represents rooms inside the house. It is set with two stools. The bed from the previous scene has been removed. A* ***muffin man*** *enters carrying a basket of muffins. He gives the basket to* ***Smith****.*

Muffin Man Ain't I seed you before?

Smith Maybe. *(Pause)* Do you know the Red Lion Tavern in Saffron Hill and the two ladies who reside there?

Muffin Man Miss Bridget and Miss Fanny who lives in the cellar, you mean? Everyone knows them!

Smith I'd be obliged if you'd carry 'em a message. Tell 'em a – a 'certain person's' well and prospering. Tell 'em 'e's on 'is way up in the world... and will communicate further when a suitable occasion has arose.

Muffin Man I'll tell 'em.

Smith Don't forget now. A certain person's on his way up in the world.

*The **muffin man** exits.*

Smith *(Talking to himself)* Well, well they aren't gone for ever. Some day, soon, Miss Bridget, Miss Fanny, Lord Tom, and me, we'll meet again, but I've got to get the information out of the document. I've got to get the document, but how? Still, Miss Mansfield says that my reading is coming on.

***Smith** exits carrying the basket and his sweeping brush.*

Chorus 1 After three weeks of living with the Mansfields, Smith has finally had an opportunity to tell his sisters and Lord Tom that he is safe.

Chorus 2 But the document still remains in Mr Mansfield's study and all Smith's wit and deftness has brought him no nearer to recovering it.

Chorus 3 For Miss Mansfield watches him like a brisk and suspicious hawk.

Chorus 1 In three weeks, Smith has come to think as well of the Mansfields, as of anyone else he might call his friends.

***Meg** enters the house, stage left. She is followed by **Smith**, who carries the basket of muffins and a book.*

Meg You got them muffins?

***Smith** gives **Meg** the basket of muffins. Then he sits on a stool and opens up his book.*

Meg Learning? Give you a farthing for it! Mark my words, my little one – a human being's better off without it! What good's it ever done a soul? Brains! Wouldn't 'ave them if you paid me. A penn'orth of heart's worth all your skinny clever heads.

Smith But at least you can read, Meg. For you read the name on that old paper you found when I was washed.

Meg *(Crossly)* I can read what's needful and proper, young man! But no more than that. F'rinstance, I never read a book.

Smith But Miss Mansfield reads!

Meg Yes! You look at the mistress. All trouble and worry and storms in the heart! And then you look at the master, who can neither read or write on account of his disability – which is maybe a blessing in disguise. All smiles and even-faced. All contentment, I'd say. There, now! So who's the better off? Brains! Give you a farthing for 'em!

***Meg** exits. **Smith** continues to read.*

Chorus 1 In spite of Meg's warnings, Smith continues to study as hard as he is able.

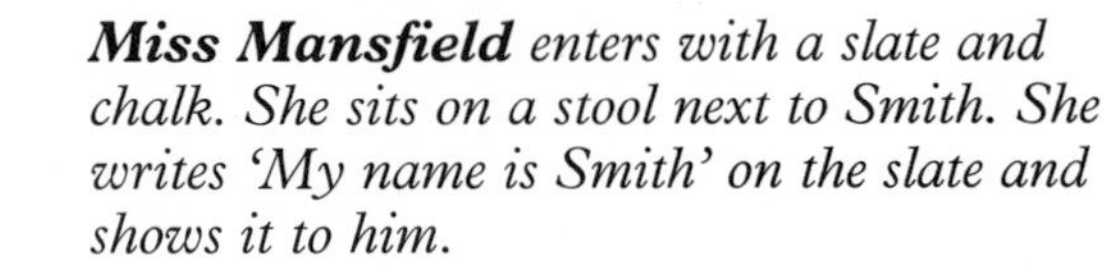
***Miss Mansfield** enters with a slate and chalk. She sits on a stool next to Smith. She writes 'My name is Smith' on the slate and shows it to him.*

Chorus 2 With Miss Mansfield's help, he masters the alphabet. That collection of twists and curls and crosses and gibbet-shaped* signs.

Smith *(Reading carefully from the slate)* M-y n-a-m-e is S-m-i-t-h.

Miss Mansfield Well done! In a short time, Smith, you will be able to read anything you wish to.

***Miss Mansfield** puts down the slate, takes the book Smith has been studying and points out words for Smith to read. **Smith** 'reads' to Miss Mansfield as the **Chorus** speak.*

Chorus 3 Miss Mansfield has grown fond of Smith. He's darted into her heart as neatly as she supposes he'd once darted from doorway to doorway.

Chorus 2 For Miss Mansfield, Smith is an extraordinary child; quick-witted, clear-faced, obliging, and determined.

Miss Mansfield Your long battle is over and all the wisdom of the world is yours for the taking. Smith, now you can read!

Smith *(Deeply surprised and grateful)* I never thought I'd do it. Can I really, miss, really read, and will I get better?

There is the sound of a knock at the door.

Smith That will be Mister Billing, miss! Come a-cooing*. So I'll be off and 'ide myself now. The best of luck to you, miss! I'm sure you'll be very 'appy.

***Smith** gets up.*

Miss Mansfield No, just you sit down where you are. I've told Mr Billing just how well you are progressing with your reading and I'm sure he'd like to hear for himself.

***Smith**, hopping and skipping, heads off stage.*

Smith But, miss...

Miss Mansfield I insist. I want Mr Billing to see what an excellent pupil I have.

Smith Can't we do this next week, miss, and then I'll be ready to read to other people.

***Mr Billing** and **Mr Mansfield** enter together, talking. **Smith** is about to dodge past them.*

Smith Best of 'appiness in your cooing, Mister Billing.

***Mr Billing** looks at Smith.*

Mr Billing That's him!

Mr Billing grabs at Smith and catches hold of him.

Mr Mansfield What?

Mr Billing This is the boy I saw in Curtis Court. This boy stabbed Field! I saw him. He is the murderer! My poor friends; how monstrously you have been deceived!

Mr Mansfield No sir, not this boy! Not Smith. Never, I tell you. You are mistaken!

Mr Billing This is the boy I saw in Curtis Court. I saw him struggle. I saw him stab. I saw him escape. There is no doubt. I wish to God there was. Forgive me.

Smith You're mad! You're mad! I never laid a finger on the old man! I never touched the old man! I never – never – never! You was wrong, Mister Billing! For Gawd's sake, tell 'em! For you're a-killing me!

Mr Billing Not wrong, Smith. I saw. I know.

Smith Then damn you! *(To Miss Mansfield)* Miss! You knows me! I never done it! Swear on the Scriptures! Swear! Swear! You believe me, Miss Mansfield? Please...

Miss Mansfield *(Turning away)* Oh, Smith!

Smith Then damn you, too! You Bedlam-mad* saint! *(To Mr Mansfield)* Mister Mansfield! You believe me, I know it. I can see it in your – your...You know me – and I know you. You know I never done him in. Mister Mansfield! You must believe! It wasn't me! It was the men in brown and...

Mr Mansfield Men in brown?

Smith Yes! Yes!

Mr Mansfield You saw them kill Mr Field?

Smith I... I...

Mr Mansfield Yet, you once told me you'd never seen Mr Field. So now we have the truth! It was you who killed him! *(Pause)* Which hand did you use, Smith? Was it the one you gave me that night we met? Was it that same, helping hand? Tell me, Smith. Don't be ashamed – for didn't I say to you that devils and angels are all one to me. *(Pause)* Well, our course is clear. You will be taken to Newgate prison to await your trial.

Smith Trial? What do you want to try me for? Might as well do me in now. You'll never see me face when I'm nubbed. Nothing'll haunt you! You done right, you have! All I 'ope is – fer your sake and mine – that if you goes to heaven, then I goes to hell! For I wouldn't want you to clap even dead eyes on me!

Mr Mansfield Smith!

Smith I never done it, Mister Mansfield!

Mr Mansfield You'll be tried.

Smith *(Alarmed)* And nubbed!

Mr Mansfield God have mercy on your soul.

Smith *(Angrily)* Not if He's a blind old gent like you!

Mr Mansfield Smith! Daughter, please ring for a footman.

***Miss Mansfield** 'rings the servants' bell'.*

Mr Billing I'll go with him to the prison.

Mr Mansfield There is no need, Billing. There's no need for you to endure any more.

Mr Billing I'll go, sir. It – it's the least I can do. Let the wretched child have some company on his journey.

*Enter **Footman 1**.*

Mr Billing *(To the footman)* Hold the boy!

*The surprised **footman** is uncertain of what to do.*

Mr Billing Don't just stand there. Smith is going to Newgate prison. Take him outside and don't let go of him.

*The **footman** holds **Smith** securely and they both exit.*

Miss Mansfield *(To Mr Billing)* We thank you, sir, for this – kindness. I blame myself for this. It was I who encouraged the boy. My father was not party to it. *(To Mr Mansfield)* Papa, you have a donkey for a daughter! A sentimental, foolish donkey! So we must be thankful to Mr Billing who's proved himself the best and truest of friends.

Mr Billing We need to have the warrant signed. I'll also get a coach.

***Mr Billing**, **Miss Mansfield**, and **Mr Mansfield** exit. In the area, stage right, the **Chorus** create a coach from boxes taken from the set. Then they step back from the action. The **coachman** enters and sits at the front of the coach. **Footman 1** enters holding **Smith**. He puts **Smith** in the coach. **Meg** enters. She is upset by the events. She waves to Smith.*

Meg I'll come and see you dear, don't fret, little Smith. Meg won't forget you, dear!

***Meg** exits. **Mr Billing** enters carrying the warrant and sits next to Smith in the coach. **Footman 1** exits.*

Mr Billing *(To the coachman)* To Newgate prison! *(To Smith)* Give it to me, boy. For God's sake, boy! There's not much time! Give it to me – the paper that you stole from the old man in Curtis Court. Let me have it – and you can go.

Smith I ain't got it.

Mr Billing And I know you have!

Smith Search me – or are you afraid of getting bit? For I'm a venomous little snake, I am!

Mr Billing All right, lad – I believe you. What was in it?

Smith Don't know.

Mr Billing Then – where is it?

Smith Don't know.

Mr Billing Don't your life mean a fig to you?

Smith Don't know.

Mr Billing You're a foolish young man. I promise I'll help you, but you must tell me. It's your only chance.

***Smith** remains silent.*

Mr Billing All right! Keep silent now, if you must. I'll understand. But believe me, young Smith, I'm your truest friend! And soon you'll come to see it. I'll visit you in Newgate and we'll talk again. Lay our cards on the table, eh? And then – and then, who knows, but we may soon be friends? You and me, Smith. Don't look so despairing, son, I'm not a villain. It's a vile world we live in, boy!

***Chorus 1** indicates the area, centre stage.*

Chorus 1 Newgate prison!

***Mr Jones**, the hangman, enters and stands, centre stage. **Smith** and **Mr Billing** get out of the coach and walk over to Mr Jones. **Mr Billing** keeps a tight hold on **Smith**. **Mr Billing** passes both the warrant and **Smith** over to **Mr Jones**, who takes hold of **Smith** by the scruff of his neck. **Mr Billing** exits. The **coachman** exits and the **Chorus** replace the boxes used for the coach.*

Mr Jones Not old Smith? Grubby Smith? Thieving Smith. Smith o' the doorways and corners? Smith o' the stinking Red Lion? But washing ain't exactly been profitable, eh? For your dirt, Smith, hid a multitude o' sins and now them sins is exposed to view, so here you are, me lad! Jailed, jugged and bottled – as we say in the trade.

***Mr Jones** puts **Smith** in handcuffs. Four **prisoners**, in chains, enter Newgate prison. Three stand looking off stage, as if they are watching events outside the prison. **Prisoner 4** sits alone in a fireplace which is part of the set. **Mr Jones** exits.*

Chorus 2 Smith's arrival at Newgate prison causes no more stir than a driblet of spittle* in the Fleet Ditch.

Chorus 3 In less than two weeks, Dick Mulrone, the famous felon, is to be taken out of Newgate and hanged.

Chorus 1 From morning to night there is a press of carriages outside the prison – for Mr Dick Mulrone has more friends and admirers than he knows what to do with.

Chorus 2 The only person to pay any heed to Smith is an old man, who has not seen daylight for fifteen years.

***Prisoner 4** beckons to Smith from the fireplace.*

Prisoner 4 This fireplace is a fine place to sleep. There's a good draught from the chimney. Look up there. *(He points upwards)* Sometimes you can see a star twinkling away, so close it could be sitting on the roof of this 'ere Newgate jail. It ain't so bad, little sparrow. You gets used to it. Though we never sees the sun, we never gets doused by the rain, neither! And it's a comfort to know you're in the worst place in the world... so you've nowt to fret and slave about to keep yourself from falling lower. For you've arrived.

***Mr Jones** enters with **Miss Bridget** and **Miss Fanny**. He removes Smith's handcuffs and exits.*

Miss Bridget The shame of it! Fine clothes and a clean face are but the trappings of shame, when the child what has them is so degradingly jugged!

Smith I never done it! You know I never done it!

Miss Bridget You're here, ain't you? That speaks volumes, don't it? You done something!

Smith I was wrongly accused! Victimized!

Miss Fanny Innocence is no excuse in the eyes of the law, Smut dear. That much your sisters know!

Miss Bridget Much good your gentility will do you when that disgusting hangman, Mr Jones, has done with you! It's your clothes that will be coming down my steps at the Red Lion Tavern with no boy in them.

Miss Fanny You should have given up the document when Lord Tom asked – or even to the fierce gents in brown.

Smith Did they come back then - them men in brown?

***Lord Tom** enters.*

Miss Fanny Yes, again and again! Haunted the Red Lion for several days. But Lord Tom spoke to them and they haven't been back since.

Lord Tom Well, Smut, me lad! It seems you got here before me! But we'll see, me fine lad! Yes, we'll see! While there's life, there's hope. Maybe Lord Tom can help?

Smith How?

Lord Tom The document, young fellow! Do you have it still?

Smith N-not with me, Lord Tom.

Lord Tom But you know where it lies?

Smith That I do, Lord Tom.

Lord Tom And, given certain circumstances – such as you might know best – could you lay your hands on the afore-mentioned property?

Smith That I could, Lord Tom!

Lord Tom And would you, me boy?

Smith That I would, Lord Tom! With all me heart!

Lord Tom Then we'll see, me bright young heart. While Lord Tom's about, there's a ray of light.

Lord Tom *offers his arms to escort the ladies out of Newgate prison. It is only* ***Miss Fanny*** *who takes up the offer.* ***Miss Fanny*** *and* ***Lord Tom*** *exit.* ***Miss Bridget*** *puts down a guinea coin for Smith.*

Miss Bridget I'll be back tomorrow, you – felonious child! Just remember... though you be... not so good as you ought... you ain't forgot. Fan and I'll be back.

Miss Bridget *exits.* ***Smith*** *notices the guinea coin and picks it up.*

Smith Who left this for me? *(To Prisoner 4)* Did you notice who left this *(Indicating the coin)* for me?

Prisoner 4 Ah, me sparrow, that would be telling, wouldn't it? Which one cares a guinea's worth? The pigeon? The starling? Or that seedy hawk? It's worse than not knowing who's done you an injury – who's done you a kindness.

Mr Billing *enters.* ***Prisoner 4*** *gives Mr Billing a look of distaste and then turns his back on him.*

Mr Billing *(To Smith)* Well, lad, as you see, I've not forgot you.

Smith No, Mister Billing, I don't suppose you 'ave. And I've not forgot you, Mister lying Billing – Mister murdering Billing. Not till Mister Jones the hangman, turns me off the road will I forget you! And if there's such a thing as ghosts, Mister conniving Billing, there'll be a shrieking ghost awaiting for you every night of your life when you goes to bed!

***Mr Billing** is taken aback.*

Mr Billing I... I'm not a bad lot, y'know. I live in the world, so to speak... and can't help being of it. Take me all in all, I'm no worse than anyone else. Believe me, young man, you'll come to see that! Life's a race for rats... and it's Devil take the hindmost, the foremost – and the one in the middle. We're all rats, Smith – and it's eat or be eaten. Blame nature, if you like – but don't blame me.

***Smith** looks at Mr Billing doubtfully.*

Mr Billing All right, then. Don't trust me. I don't blame you. If I was in your position I'd be just as suspicious. But, I tell you here and now, my friend, I saved your life.

Smith By having me nubbed?

Mr Billing They knew you were with the Mansfields in Vine Street.

Smith Who did?

Mr Billing The men in brown. And they'd have come to murder you if I'd done nothing and left you there.

Smith Ain't they your friends, then, Mister Billing?

Mr Billing Listen, friend. I'll lay my cards on the table. Open and above board. I'll not lie to you – for I like you. We're two of a kind, Smith, you and me. Men who know what's what in the world. Eyes open, chins up – and outface the Devil.

Smith Did they 'ave to kill the old man?

Mr Billing Ask Mr Black, my friend.

Smith *(Chilled)* Was he the other one? Who was there at the murder in Curtis Court? The one who organized it? The one with the limp?

Mr Billing More than a limp, Smith. A wooden leg. A very devil. Right, lad! I'll lay my cards on the table. That document is worth money. A vast deal of money. Enough for you and me and the chimney-sweep down the road. I mean our friend, Mr Black.

Mr Billing For I tell you, I see no way of keeping him out of it. None! He's got the pair of us, Smith! We're the little running rats – and he's the gobbling devil! If only – ah, if only...

Smith If only what, Mister Billing?

Mr Billing You and me... you and me... Where did you leave the document?

Smith In...

__Prisoner 4__ suddenly bangs his chains on the floor. __Smith__ stops speaking and realizes that he could easily have said too much.

Mr Billing Where, Smith? Where?

Smith Lorst me memory, Mister Billing.

Mr Billing What do you mean?

Smith Strain of waiting to be nubbed, Mister Billing. Can't remember a thing. Leastways not while I'm 'ere.

Mr Billing Don't you trust me, friend?

Smith No, Mister Billing. I've had enough of trust to last the rest of me life.

Mr Billing I suggest that you sleep on it, Smith. It may help your memory. I'll see you tomorrow.

__Mr Billing__ exits through the group of prisoners.

Smith *(Contemptuously)* Men of the world! Billing and me! But I ain't got what he wants. What does Billing want to know from that cursed document?

The __prisoners__ suddenly become excited and snatches of conversation can be heard.

Prisoner 1 Dick Mulrone has been pardoned!

Prisoner 2 No!

Prisoner 1 That's what they say!

Prisoner 3 Are you sure?

Prisoner 1 Think so!

Prisoner 3 Dick Mulrone, pardoned.

Prisoner 2 No pardon for Dick Mulrone! No pardon, that's what is being said.

Prisoner 1 Has Dick Mulrone's appeal been turned down?

Prisoner 3 No pardon for Dick Mulrone!

Prisoner 2 Dick Mulrone is to be hanged in twelve days!

Prisoner 3 Dick Mulrone to be hanged!

*The **prisoners** are upset by this news. They exit. **Smith** sits down, draws his knees up into a hunched position and drops his head forward. The **Chorus** move closer to him.*

Chorus 1 During his first nights in Newgate, Smith often dreams of the Devil and the terms he might get for his soul.

Chorus 2 He has long conversations with the Devil, who offers him escape, vengeance on the Mansfields, and enough money for himself, Mr Billing, and the chimney-sweep down the road –

Chorus 3 – all in return for a little frying.

Chorus 1 Mr Billing comes to see Smith each day, sometimes only for minutes, but other times for an hour or more.

***Prisoner 4** gets up from his fireplace and moves over to Smith.*

Prisoner 4 You ain't got it, have you?

Smith Got what?

Prisoner 4 What that legal gent wants, oh so very much!

Smith You don't know what you are talking about!

Prisoner 4 If you ain't got it, you'll have to stay!

Smith You mind yer own business!

Prisoner 4 Ain't got none to mind.

Smith If I stays they'll nub me!

Prisoner 4 *moves away from Smith and returns to his fireplace.*

Chorus 3 The date for Smith's trial has been set.

Chorus 2 Tuesday, January 23rd, the very day they are to hang Dick Mulrone.

Smith Oh Gawd! Why did the old gent have to stuff his pockets with such deadly papers? What right 'ad 'e to go walking the streets, 'eavy with the Devil's literature for to tempt the likes of me with?

Smith *groans in misery. The* ***Chorus*** *move away as* ***Meg*** *enters, carrying a bundle.*

Meg You poor thing. Oh, you poor thing! You've grown smaller and wizender. Here, I've brought you some veal pie, sausage and bread. *(She hands the bundle to* ***Smith****)* You needs feeding up, and not meaning to be personal, dear – you needs another good wash. Cleverness! Look where it gets you. I'll wager there's enough cleverness in here to sink London Bridge! Brains? Give you a farthing for 'em! You poor thing!

Smith They're going to hang me, Meg.

Meg Oh, you poor thing!

Smith There's but one soul who can save me, Meg.

Meg Ah, the master!

Smith No, Meg. You!

Meg If heart can save you, child – then it's done. But this is a wicked world of cleverness.

Smith It's heart I need, Meg, for it's cleverness what put me 'ere.

Meg Say on.

Smith Do you recall the paper you found when I was first washed? Is it still where you put it?

Meg Most likely.

Smith Can you get it for me?

Meg Why, child, it's the master's!

Smith No, Meg, it was mine. And it's the only thing that will save me.

Meg I... I couldn't steal from the master!

Smith But it was mine!

Meg It's all a nasty piece of cleverness, child. You'd be best off without it! Believe Meg!

***Smith** is upset.*

Smith Meg... Meg! You're hanging me! True as we're 'ere! If I don't get it, I'll be buried afore spring!

Meg Oh, little one. I don't know what to do! Oh, Lord! What would me mother have said? 'Follow your heart, Meg!' Well, that's it.

Meg Follow your heart! *(Tearfully)* I'll fetch you the paper, little Smith, and may it save your poor neck from the noose!

***Meg** kisses **Smith** on the cheek and exits.*

Smith *(Triumphantly)* Well, Mister Billing, now that I practically have the document, it won't be so long before you and I can strike a bargain and a little bird can fly out of this stone cage.

*The **Chorus** move closer to Smith.*

Chorus 1 Smith considers himself as good as out of jail and the change in his manner is as astonishing as abrupt.

Smith *(To himself)* Oh, I'll be happy going!

***Mr Billing** enters. **Smith** jumps up cheerfully.*

Chorus 3 Mr Billing sees this change in Smith. He notices Meg's bundle and wonders if Smith already has the document. He smiles knowingly.

Chorus 2 Smith sees Mr Billing's look and guesses what he is thinking. He shakes his head and grins.

Smith *(Putting down the bundle)* Not yet, Mister Billing.

Mr Billing *(To Smith)* How much better it is to put our cards on the table – play fair – and be friends. Oh, the world's not such a bad place after all, for the likes of you and me.

*While the **Chorus** speak, **Smith** and **Mr Billing** freeze as though in deep and secret conversation.*

Chorus 2 The days pass. Monday, January the 15th comes, and brings heavy snow – there seems to be no end to it.

Chorus 3 Visitors to Newgate are few and far between, only Smith's sisters and the ever-faithful Mr Billing. Smith waits uneasily on Meg returning with the document.

Chorus 1 Hurry, Meg; time is getting short.

Chorus 2 Smith worries that Mr Billing is impatient to get the document and is becoming suspicious –

Chorus 3 – though nothing is said. It's as though Mr Billing won't act until he knows the outcome of some other event.

Chorus 1 Then, on Friday, Mr Billing seems to have made up his mind. He offers Smith a plan of escape.

*The **Chorus** move away from the action.*

Mr Billing Smith, I think that friendship comes before everything else, so I have a small secret to share with you that should see you out of here.

***Mr Billing** takes a piece of paper out of his pocket. It is a rough plan of Newgate's ventilation shafts which lead to the roof.*

Mr Billing Here's a map of the prison building and the ventilation tunnels. Not too long ago there was set up on the roof of the prison a windmill with vanes full twenty feet across. Its purpose is to purify the air. As it turns it draws up much of the foul vapour of this building through ventilation shafts that honeycomb the building. There are a great many narrow tunnels that lead through dark and angled ways to the great shaft that rises to the windmill. The lower tunnels are narrow, but wide enough for a thin one. From the roof it is but a hop, jump, and scramble to the adjoining roofs.

***Mr Billing** gives the map to **Smith**.*

Smith When am I to go?

Mr Billing Patience! Not yet. Study the map and the route out.

Smith So, when am I to leave?

Mr Billing When this grating is unlocked. *(He indicates the 'ventilation grating' close to the fireplace)* A certain gentleman will make sure that the grating is unlocked for your escape.

Smith When's it to be?

Mr Billing On Tuesday.

Smith Why so long?

Mr Billing It is only four more days.

Smith Why not before?

Mr Billing Tuesday will be a day of great commotion. Dick Mulrone sets forth to be hanged at Tyburn Hill. Jailers and turnkeys* will be busy keeping order – too busy to notice a little bird fly out of his cage. Tuesday, at six o'clock in the morning. Just before you are supposed to be moved to the session house for your trial. Listen for the bell. Six o'clock. Tuesday will be freedom day, and of course, document day, Smith. Farewell!

__Mr Billing__ exits. __Smith__ puts the map in his pocket.

Smith Come on, Meg, I need you to bring the document! You can't let me down, not now. Mister Billing seemed so confident and he's nobody's fool. The grating will be open, Tuesday, at six o'clock.

__Meg__ enters and approaches Smith. She stands looking downhearted.

Smith Have you – have you got the document, Meg? *(Pause)* Meg, where is it?

Meg Oh child! They'll hang you now for sure, and bury you afore the spring.

Smith *(Desperately)* Meg! Where is it?

Meg Heart weren't enough. On Thursday, the master and mistress went out together; so I took me chance, and crept like a mouse into the study. I was in the master's study when I heard a noise from upstairs, where you used to sleep. I crept out and up the stairs. Sure enough, there was noise coming from your room; scraping – dragging – pulling – panting, like it was being torn apart by dumb beasts. I was frightened! I thought that maybe a bear had got in!

Smith What was it, Meg?

Meg I screamed, child! That I did. Screamed and shrieked till Vine Street echoed. I got a good pair of lungs.

Smith And – then?

Meg It must have scared 'em.

Smith Who?

Meg Two horrible men dressed in brown. They burst out of the room in a terrible rage! I thought they'd kill me – but they rushed past me and down the stairs, then out through the front door like the wind o' hell!

Smith *(To himself)* That's why Billing came here with his plan. The men in brown had failed to get the document. If he wants it now, he's got to get me out!

Meg *(Tearfully)* So there's no hope. Mr Mansfield has locked all his papers away.

Smith *(Bewildered)* No more hope?

Meg The burglary has so upset the master that he's locked all his papers securely away. There's nothing I can do.

Smith *(Cheerfully)* Never worry, Meg.

Meg Why, Smith, you ain't downhearted! You'll go straight to heaven, no matter what you done! I must go now, and I promise to try to help no matter.

Smith Thank you, Meg!

***Meg** exits. **Prisoner 4** moves from his fireplace towards Smith.*

Prisoner 4 You've not got it yet, have you?

Smith No, I ain't. But neither has he! That lawyer thought he'd have Smith for his dinner. He thought I was easy. And his friends in brown! Wish I'd seen their faces! Wish I'd seen his face when

Smith they told him what luck they'd had. If he wants the document, and he thinks I know where it is, then that grating will be open. Keep smiling Smith! *(He looks towards the 'grating')* Soon be out of here!

Prisoner 4 *(Pointing to the 'grating')* Won't be long now, then!

Chorus 1 Monday evening – Smith has a visitor.

***Mr Jones** enters.*

Mr Jones Visitor for Smith! Look lively! Visitor!

***Miss Mansfield** enters and **Mr Jones** exits.*

Smith *(Anxiously to himself)* Why has Miss Mansfield come here?

Chorus 2 Has Mr Billing confided the whole plan to Miss Mansfield who is here to wreck it?

Miss Mansfield Smith! You've grown vastly dirty again!

Smith Mister Jones won't mind...

Miss Mansfield Who's he?

Smith The 'angman!

Miss Mansfield I would help you!

*She tries to embrace **Smith** but he avoids her. **Miss Mansfield** appeals to Prisoner 4.*

Miss Mansfield I would help him!

Prisoner 4 He don't need your help, ma'am.

Smith What do you want with me? Keep off! Leave me alone!

Miss Mansfield Don't hate us!

***Mr Jones** enters.*

Mr Jones Blind man! Blind man! Make way.

Mr Mansfield *enters.* ***Miss Mansfield*** *goes to help him, but she is annoyed that he has followed her.*

Miss Mansfield Father, you said that you would stay in the carriage!

Mr Mansfield Daughter! Is he here?

Miss Mansfield Yes, sir.

Mr Mansfield *draws the document out of his coat pocket.*

Mr Mansfield Smith, do you know what this is?

Miss Mansfield *speaks quietly as she explains.*

Miss Mansfield Meg told us. In tears she came – poor soul. She said it was the only thing that would save you.

Mr Mansfield *holds out the document.*

Mr Mansfield Do you know what it is, Smith?

Smith No! No! Never seen it before!

Mr Mansfield Look again. Look closely. Look hard.

Smith To Mister Lennard, Billing and Lennard of Curtis Court, Godliman Street. Never – seen – it – before!

Mr Mansfield Mr Lennard is at Mr Field's house at Prickler's Hill. I'm taking this document to him, Smith.

Smith W-what's in it then?

Mr Mansfield I do not know. It's for Mr Lennard. A dead man's wish, Smith. Binding. It will be delivered tomorrow.

Miss Mansfield And let's hope and pray, Smith, that it will indeed save you!

Mr Mansfield Mr Billing will apply for an adjournment of your trial. I have asked him...

Smith *(Almost screaming)* Then he knows you've got the document?

Mr Mansfield He knows no more than I've told him. Why should he? This is Mr Lennard's affair.

***Mr Mansfield** and **Miss Mansfield** exit.*

Smith *(Shouting after them)* Billing knows! You blind old fool! They'll kill you! Blind right through you are!

***Smith** lies down and tries to rest. The **Chorus** move forward.*

Chorus 1 There are a few hours left before the escape, but with Mr Billing now knowing who has the document, would the grating be unlocked for Smith to squeeze through?

Chorus 2 It's quarter to six in the morning, the day Dick Mulrone is to be hanged.

***Prisoner 4** gets up and wakes **Smith**.*

Prisoner 4 It's time to go.

They both move to the 'grating' by the fireplace.

Prisoner 4 Up you go.

Smith What if it ain't unlocked?

Prisoner 4 It's been done.

Smith When?

Prisoner 4 While you slept, I heard. Come, now up and in you go.

Smith *(Pausing)* D'you think you could come too?

Prisoner 4 Don't want to. This is me home. Got company.

Smith I'll not be seeing you more...

Prisoner 4 I hopes not! Go on with you!

Smith Hopes you gets a gentleman for the fireplace that suits.

Prisoner 4 That's my affair!

Smith No offence.

Prisoner 4 None took. Go on, you scabby little sparrow!

__Prisoner 4__ exits. Carefully, __Smith__ 'opens the grating' and climbs onto the raised part of the stage. His journey through the ventilation shafts takes him across the back of the stage, through the clutter of the set. Eventually he crouches and looks up. The __Chorus__ move close to Smith.

Chorus 1 Bruised and much fouled from his journey, Smith crouches in the last bend and stares triumphantly up. Fifteen feet above him hang the motionless vanes of the ventilation windmill, folded now in snow. Beyond is the grey sky. He stops.

Chorus 2 There is an oddness about the lip of the shaft. A ragged irregularity that seems to be growing two swellings. Heads! Two men! A pair of hands reach down for him. Fingers twitch and beckon. The men in brown!

Chorus 3 Smith lets go of his hold and drops down – choking, bumping, to the bottom of the steep shaft – through a vent that leads to a quiet passage way.

__Smith__ 'drops down the shaft'. He rolls and bumps down, choking as he goes. He comes to a stop and gets up.

Smith Got to get out! Got to get out!

Off stage, there is the sound of a crowd approaching.

Smith They're coming along this way!

Smith *hides as a crowd of people enter from the back of the stage.*
The crowd includes ***Mr Jones, a priest, Dick Mulrone*** *(the highwayman),* ***Lord Tom,*** *who walks close to Dick Mulrone,* ***Miss Bridget*** *and* ***Miss Fanny****. They are on their way to Dick Mulrone's hanging.*

Miss Fanny A good sermon that priest gave about the handsome Dick Mulrone.

Miss Bridget Much good may it do him. He's on his way to be hanged!

Miss Fanny I do enjoy a good hanging! You meet people!

Miss Bridget *holds her sister back. The crowd move on and exit.*

Miss Bridget I'm here for Dick Mulrone's clothes. Which way is it Mr Jones said we should go to find them?

Smith *emerges from his hiding place.*

Smith *(In hushed tones)* Brid! Over here.

Miss Bridget Smut! It's Smut!

Miss Fanny Smut! What are you doing here?

Smith Got to get out.

Miss Bridget Quick, under my skirt child! Pop underneath and not a sound. There'll be others coming down this way!

Blackout.

Scene 6

Lights up. The area stage right is set as the cellar of the Red Lion Tavern. ***Miss Bridget*** *and* ***Miss Fanny*** *are sitting on stools, sewing clothes.* ***Smith*** *is explaining to his sisters and* ***Lord Tom*** *what happened when he tried to escape from Newgate prison by climbing the ventilation shafts. The* ***Chorus*** *are visible, watching the action.*

Smith Two men dressed in brown were waiting for me on the roof. Waiting to haul me out of the ventilation shaft. I couldn't go up and the only other way was down! Billing had set a trap for me! He wants to silence me for good! We've got to help Mister Mansfield, Lord Tom!

Lord Tom If what you say, Smith, is true then we need to stop Mr Mansfield on his way to deliver the document to Mr Field's house at Prickler's Hill.

Smith We have to warn him about the men in brown and Mister Billing. They will kill him for the document.

Lord Tom We have to warn him of the danger he's in!

Smith How do we do that, Lord Tom?

Lord Tom Well, given the sort of coach Mr Mansfield uses, given this weather, given the crowds out watching for Dick Mulrone on his way to being nubbed – your Mr Mansfield will probably take luncheon at the Queen's Head in Lamb's Conduit Fields, and come upon the Common at half after four. And at five, we'll have him.

Miss Fanny *(Admiringly)* Lord Tom, I just knew that you could sort it out.

Smith Ye-es, Lord Tom, if someone else don't have him first!

Lord Tom D'you mean our friends in brown?

Miss Fanny Lord Tom'll see them off, Smut. You'll see!

Lord Tom I'll blow blue daylight through them, Smut!

Miss Fanny And then – our document, at last!

Miss Bridget That document! How I hate and despise it! It brought an old man to his death and made murderers of nought but common thieves. And now to take a child onto a murdering Common for to rob a blind man. Shame!

Lord Tom What can I do? You've heard the lad, he's determined.

Smith That document can prevent me from goin' down in the world.

Miss Fanny If his heart's set on going, Bridget dear, 'tis wicked to thwart him! By tonight, we'll have the document safe and sound and Smut'll read it to us!

Lord Tom Nothing any of us say will prevent him from this venture. Well, Smut, me comrade in arms of this day! Are we fit and ready? Make your adieus, Smut – then it's the Common for both of us!

Smith *moves to stand with Lord Tom.*

Miss Bridget But he'll freeze to death! He cannot go so ill dressed!

Miss Bridget *takes a cloak from the pile of clothes waiting to be sewn and puts it round* ***Smith*****.** ***Smith*** *starts to leave the cellar, but turns and addresses his sisters in his best highwayman voice.*

Smith Adieu, dear ladies! Wish me...

Miss Bridget Smut! All those brave highwaymen, who once waited on the Common and pounced, are come to a bad end at Tyburn Hill. There's no heroism or gallantry in being one of...

Lord Tom *(Interrupting)* Gallantry, ma'am, there's gallantry on the Common! Fierce beauty and soaring adventure. Wild nights with gentlemen of the road! Duval...

Miss Bridget Hanged!

Lord Tom Turpin...

Miss Bridget Hanged!

Lord Tom Captain Robinson...

Miss Bridget Hanged!

Lord Tom Yes, ma'am, they paid for their joys. They're dead and gone... and so've a great many other folk. 'Tis the common penalty for living. But it's not the quiet mewing, moaning, bed perishings that haunt the Common of a moony night. No ma'am! When we ride out, we ride with a great ghostly company of the nubbed.

Miss Bridget Shame on you! We don't want to hear of your adventures yet again.

Smith Isn't it time to be off, Lord Tom?

Miss Bridget You take care of our Smut, Lord Tom.

Lord Tom I'll guard him, ma'am, with my very life, I do assure you. While he's with Lord Tom, no danger will offer. Come lad!

__Lord Tom__ and __Smith__ exit from the cellar. Blackout.

Scene 7

Lights up. The area centre stage is now Finchley Common. It is covered with snow. There are two inns either side of the Common. The area stage left is Bob's Inn, and is set with a table or box, some stools, bottles, tankards, and a spy glass. __Bob__, the innkeeper, is in position, tidying up. The area stage right is The Wrestler's Inn. Here, the two __men in brown__ sit waiting, wrapped up against the cold. The __Chorus__ are visible, watching the action. __Lord Tom__ and __Smith__ enter and walk towards Bob's Inn.

Chorus 1 Bob's Inn. Highgate Hill. Overlooking Finchley Common.

Lord Tom The weather! The snow! And the cold! But here we are; here we are Smith – Bob's Inn.

Smith *(Indicating the area, centre stage)* Is this the Common?

Lord Tom Aye! And we are early, so it's a drink by a warm fire.

***Lord Tom** and **Smith** enter Bob's Inn. **Bob** welcomes them.*

Bob Ah! Lord Tom. I see you have a brisk, bright and prosperous apprentice to the 'Trade', with you! Nothing coming, nothing going. *(In a knowing way)* Not our sort of weather, eh, Lord Tom? Come, warm yourselves by the fire. Jars of the best?

Lord Tom There's a coach due, Bob, within this half an hour. From town toward Barnet.

Bob You know best, friend. You got a reputation. But it surprises me, yes indeed. Must be powerful business to draw a coach across this murderous white nothingness.

Lord Tom *(Winking at Smith)* It is. It surely is. Smut, I have a little business to attend to across the way at The Wrestler's Inn. Just stay here for a while and don't move under any circumstances.

Bob He'll be fine here with me. He can watch the road with the spy glass.

Lord Tom That's a good idea. Sixpence for the use of the glass, Bob.

***Lord Tom** offers Bob a coin.*

Bob Keep your money, friend. On an evening like this I'm all for the warmth of kindness. The lad can watch for free.

Lord Tom There, Smut. There's a small taste of the companionship. You're among friends! Watch out for the coach, Smut!

***Lord Tom** leaves Bob's Inn and moves across the stage to The Wrestler's Inn. He sits down with the men in brown.*

Bob *(To Smith)* That Lord Tom's a grand fellow! One of the best.

***Bob** picks up the spy glass and gives it to **Smith**.*

Bob Take it, lad! Go and watch for the coach. And remember, through that self same glass the proudest, sharpest, most gallantest eyes these parts have ever known, once stared. Go stand by the window. D'you see that long shadowy finger? That's the road the coach'll come by... if it comes.

***Bob** moves away and continues his tidying up. **Smith** looks through the spy glass in the direction of the Common for a few moments. At The Wrestler's Inn, **Lord Tom** is now having a hushed conversation with the two **men in brown**.*

Smith It's coming! Lord Tom had best be quick!

***Smith** turns the spy glass and looks towards The Wrestler's Inn.*

Smith Make haste, Lord Tom, the coach is sighted! Hurry, friend of mine! Get up off your chair and leave those...

***Smith** sees the men in brown. He also sees that **Lord Tom** is scared of them.*

Smith Lord Tom! What's happened to you. Why are you looking so humble? Why are you cringing to those men? You're frightened! You're frightened by those men in brown!

***Bob** overhears the last part of what Smith says.*

Bob What's amiss, lad?

Smith Nothing! You mind your own damned business, Mister Bob – and I'll mind mine.

Bob Getting nervous are you? First time on the Common? I'll fetch you a tot of brandy, lad. That'll put fire into you, for your 'stand and deliver!'

__Bob__ turns to pour Smith a drink. __Smith__ exits quickly from Bob's Inn. __Bob__ turns back with the drink and sees __Smith__ leaving.

Bob Come back! Come back!

__Bob__ follows __Smith__. They both exit. Blackout.

• •

Scene 8

Lights up. The area centre stage still represents Finchley Common. It is snowing hard. To the left of this area, a coach has been created by boxes taken from the set. The area stage right is now the Parkins' cottage. It is set with a table bearing a bottle and glasses, and a couple of stools. There is also a candlestick on the table. __Mr Mansfield__ is sitting in the coach. The __coachman__ is struggling to keep the coach moving through the snow. __Smith__ enters running. He keeps looking behind him to be sure that he is ahead of the men in brown and Lord Tom. The __Chorus__ are visible.

Chorus 2 In places the snow is two feet deep so Smith's tracks are instantly filled in after him.

Chorus 1 Through the blinding blizzard Smith battles on, closely followed by Lord Tom and the men in brown.

Chorus 3 Smith knows that he has to get to Mr Mansfield before they do or Mr Mansfield will be a dead man and the document lost forever.

Smith Coachman, stop! Stop!

Chorus 2 Thirty yards... twenty yards... the coach!

__Smith__ runs to the coach. He climbs onto it and pulls at __Mr Mansfield__.

Smith Quick, come with me!

Mr Mansfield Who's there? Who is it! My God! What do you want with me?

__Smith__ disguises his voice and puts his hand over __Mr Mansfield's__ mouth.

Smith Quiet! If you values your life!

__Smith__ drags __Mr Mansfield__ out of the coach and into a hiding place amongst the set.

Chorus 3 Smith drags Mr Mansfield into the deep drifts that lie at the side of the road.

The __coachman__ realizes that something has happened. He gets down and checks inside the coach. Finding Mr Mansfield gone, he starts to exit. __Lord Tom__ and the two __men in brown__ enter. They see the __coachman__ about to leave the stage and fire their pistols in his direction. Then they move to the coach and examine it.

Man in Brown 1 The lousy coach is empty!

Man in Brown 2 That boy of yours – he beat us to it!

Lord Tom Friends! I swear I did what I could.

Man in Brown 1 Not enough! Not enough! You should have slit his mean throat – you windbag!

Lord Tom Friends – friends! How was I to know?

Man in Brown 2 You swore you'd fix him!

Lord Tom And so I meant to! I swear it!

Man in Brown 2 Swear it to Mr Black! If he gives you leave! You'll bleed for this!

Lord Tom No! They must be near at hand! Let's search!

Man in Brown 1 In this great 'owling blizzard?

Lord Tom Then what's to be done?

Man in Brown 2 On to Mr Black in the morning. That's what.

Lord Tom But... but...

Man in Brown 2 'But' to your heart's content. Your day's done. You blotted yore book. Maybe with blood, eh?

__Lord Tom__ and the __men in brown__ exit. __Smith__ gets up, takes hold of __Mr Mansfield's__ hand and pulls him to his feet. The __Chorus__ dismantle the coach replacing any boxes and stools used in the set. __Smith__ and __Mr Mansfield__ walk around the stage, miming the action described by the __Chorus__.

Chorus 3 Four miles to the north lies Prickler's Hill. Smith sets his face in that direction and, with his hand firmly about the blind man's wrist, begins to walk.

Chorus 1 In the snow they make slow progress: in two hours something less than three quarters of a mile.

Mr Mansfield Speak then, speak... anything at all... anything!

Chorus 2 No matter how often Mr Mansfield asks who it is leading him and why he has saved him, Smith never answers.

Mr Mansfield A fine pair – we two! One with no tongue to tell what he sees – and the other with no eyes to see what's worth the telling.

Exhausted, __Smith__ and __Mr Mansfield__ rest. __Smith__ releases Mr Mansfield's wrist and moves away from him.

Smith *(Thinking aloud)* Why am I helping him?

Chorus 3 Mr Mansfield is harsh when it comes to justice. As soon as he knows who is leading him, that will be it. Handed over to the law.

Smith *(To himself)* Without a word I'll be back in Newgate prison waiting to be tried and then nubbed.

Chorus 2 There seems nothing to be gained from helping the old man – and in this weather and him blind!

Mr Mansfield *(Crying out)* Am I alone?

Chorus 1 Smith cannot just leave the old man whose desolate face speaks of a soul that has been nourished on thin fare for the past twelve years.

Smith *returns and offers Mr Mansfield a helping hand.*

Smith You blind Justice, you! Give us your hand, then! Here – here, then both me hands. You ain't alone, Mister Mansfield – nor never was. I... I was only resting.

Mr Mansfield Smith – Smith – Smith! Your voice at last! How I longed to hear it!

Smith You knew it was me, then?

Mr Mansfield Yes – yes!

Smith Then – why didn't you say?

Mr Mansfield You didn't want me to know, did you?

Smith No. I was thinking you'd 'and me over to the law.

Mr Mansfield And even so you came back?

Smith I'm only a human being.

Mr Mansfield Only!

Smith We best be moving – or we'll freeze!

Smith *and* ***Mr Mansfield*** *carry on walking.*

Chorus 1 They stumble on but no longer in silence. A curious warmth has sprung up between them that makes the wind and weather seem less savage.

Mr Mansfield Miss Mansfield has remained at home, thank God. She has avoided all this and will be able to attend your trial and keep Mr Billing to his promise of getting an adjournment.

Smith She is a saint, Mister Mansfield, a saint.

*Suddenly, **Smith** points towards the area stage right.*

Smith Hey! A cottage, Mister Mansfield!

Mr Mansfield Good.

***Charlie Parkin** and **Mrs Parkin** enter and position themselves in the area stage right.*

Smith Light in the windows. Snug little place. Looks warm. Probably a woodcutter's cottage. What say we knock on the door?

Mr Mansfield Don't mind if we do.

***Smith** and **Mr Mansfield** make their way to the Parkins' cottage. **Smith** knocks on the 'door'. **Charlie Parkin** shouts.*

Charlie Parkin Who's there? What do you want?

Smith Shelter, for a blind man and boy.

Mrs Parkin Have a look, Charlie.

***Charlie Parkin** 'opens the door'.*

Charlie Parkin Blind man and boy right enough!

***Mrs Parkin** moves close to her husband.*

Mrs Parkin I don't like it, Charlie.

Charlie Parkin No more do I, Mrs P. Shall I shut 'em out?

Mr Mansfield Good God, sir! In humanity's name! On such a night!

Charlie Parkin Did you hear that, Mrs P? The weather, y'know!

Smith Mrs P, we're frozen near to death and my friend's as blind as a post.

Mrs Parkin Charlie! See if he's blind!

***Charlie Parkin** moves warily towards **Mr Mansfield** who takes off his glasses to show his blind eyes.*

Charlie Parkin Blind all right, Mrs P!

Mrs Parkin Let them in, Charlie! Ain't you got no humanity, sir? Oh, you're a weak vessel, Charlie Parkin!

***Smith** and **Mr Mansfield** enter the Parkins' cottage. **Charlie Parkin** 'closes the door'.*

Mrs Parkin Hat! Coats! Boots! Into the kitchen with them before we're drowned out again!

***Smith** and **Mr Mansfield** take off their wet things and give them to **Charlie Parkin**.*

Charlie Parkin *(Taking the wet things off stage)* Least said, soonest mended.

Mrs Parkin You poor things! Lost your ways on the Common, I suppose?

Mr Mansfield Our coach was held up by highwaymen.

Mrs Parkin *(Calling off stage)* Charlie! They was held up! Highwaymen!

***Charlie Parkin** enters holding a pistol. His eyes are fiery.*

Charlie Parkin Highwaymen? Where?

Mrs Parkin No, no! They was held up by highwaymen. Victims, Charlie. And come to us for help!

Charlie Parkin (*Lowering his pistol*) Those damned high tobies!

Mrs Parkin Fetch the book, Charlie.

***Charlie Parkin** exits and **Mrs Parkin** calls after him.*

Mrs Parkin Ink and a fresh pen. Brown paper, Charlie.

***Charlie Parkin** returns with pen, paper and ink which he puts down on the table. He sits down on a stool, ready to write.*

Mrs Parkin Now, Charlie, off you go. Get writing! Do your job! *(Pause)* Blind man and boy. Held up – where was you held up?

Mr Mansfield On the Common, ma'am.

Mrs Parkin On the Common, Charlie.

Charlie Parkin On the Common, Mrs P. Two 'M's and one 'N'.

Mrs Parkin Robbed?

Mr Mansfield No, ma'am.

Mrs Parkin Not robbed, Charlie. Injured?

Mr Mansfield Our coachman was – murdered, I believe.

Mrs Parkin Coachman murdered, Charlie.

***Mrs Parkin** pours brandy for Smith and Mr Mansfield to drink.*

Charlie Parkin Them damned high tobies.

***Mrs Parkin** hands the drinks to **Mr Mansfield** and **Smith**.*

Mrs Parkin Two measures of brandy, Charlie!

***Charlie Parkin** continues to write.*

Charlie Parkin Two measures of brandy, Charlie. And two suppers to follow, Mrs P?

Mrs Parkin Two suppers, Charlie – and two seats by the fire for the night.

Charlie Parkin Names? What names, please?

Mr Mansfield Mr Mansfield. Justice of the Peace, sir.

Charlie Parkin A magistrate. Fancy that, Mrs P. Well, sir, it seems we're in the same line of business, for I'm a constable, among other things. Yes, sir! Here to keep law and order. And let me tell you, sir, there's not a vagabond, rogue or footpad*, who dares to set foot across the fence.

Mrs Parkin That's right. The cottage and all the land enclosed by the fence belongs to the parish – and we keep it clean and above board. The law's respected here, sir.

Charlie Parkin And everything's recorded. Accounts square and trim.

Mrs Parkin A name for honesty.

Charlie Parkin And neatness.

Mrs Parkin Come on, Charlie, we've work to do, so we cannot spend time chatting. Come on, move on, Charlie.

***Charlie Parkin** picks up the pen, paper and ink. **Mrs Parkin** ushers him off stage. **Mr Mansfield** and **Smith** sit down at the table. **Mr Mansfield** takes out the document and passes it to **Smith**.*

Mr Mansfield Here, Smith. Isn't this something you wanted? Take it and tell me what Mr Field had to say. Read it. Aloud. Don't be afraid. Read!

Smith It's a letter. It's from – Mr Field. Mr Field is afraid. He knows that he is in danger!

***Smith** reads out loud certain parts of the letter.*

Smith 'I lie awake of nights, Mr Lennard and hear such sounds and have such thoughts.' *(Pause)* Mr Field says that he made a discovery – but it don't say what – 'the trifle' – that word is underlined – 'I wrote you of previously is buried in a shrewd place. Andrews knows where. Ask him where Jack used to play as a boy. When you have it, dispose of it as it pleases you. I shall no longer care – What I have discovered, I shall take to my grave, where it will be hidden and forgot for ever.' *(Pause)* There is no more.

Mr Mansfield Nothing?

Smith Nothing! Or d'you think I'm hiding the rest from you?

Mr Mansfield The discovery! What was it?

Smith Took it with him to his grave.

Mr Mansfield Poor Mr Field. He had such an unlucky life. One child – a boy, Jack. The one he talks about in the letter. Jack disappeared; he's probably dead by now, too. So, when Mr Field died, the rest of the relations started laying siege to his house and property looking for the old man's money. They are like vultures. It is even rumoured that they know more about Jack's disappearance than they let on. We must know! The discovery! The discovery? We must know it, Smith. There'll be no peace!

Smith You find out on your own, Mister Mansfield. I'm done with it. I'm off.

Mr Mansfield But I'm blind, Smith I... I need your eyes...

Smith Your daughter's eyes are just as sharp.

Mr Mansfield Not so. They are partial, dimmed by affection. Yours, Smith, are clear.

Smith True enough.

Mr Mansfield What did you hope to get by the document? Great riches? Power? What was it Smith that you struggled so hugely for?

***Smith** remains silent.*

Mr Mansfield Smith!

Smith I'm here.

Mr Mansfield I thought you'd gone. You said you were going. Have you changed your mind?

Smith I'll go in the morning.

There is a pause.

Chorus 1 There'll be no rest.

Chorus 2 The letter says that Andrews knows something. Andrews who used to work for Mr Field at Prickler's Hill.

Smith *(Almost to himself)* What did I want from the document? Not sure really; I just hoped that it would help me to make my way in the world, I suppose.

***Smith** puts his head down on the table and begins to fall asleep.*

Chorus 3 What had Mr Field discovered? Why was he killed so coldly?

Smith *(Mumbling, half-asleep)* There'll be no peace till I know...

Blackout.

....

Scene 9

*Lights up. The area stage right is clear, and **Smith** and **Mr Mansfield** are in position there, ready to begin their journey to Mr Field's house at Prickler's Hill. The area stage left is now Mr Field's house. The **Chorus** are visible. **Smith** and **Mr Mansfield** start to walk in the direction of the house.*

Chorus 2 Just in case they are being followed, Mr Mansfield and Smith leave the coach at some distance from the house at Prickler's Hill and proceed on foot.

Smith Pistols, Mister Mansfield, perhaps we should have brought them with us from the coach?

Mr Mansfield The gentlemen from Highgate Hill seem to have given up. No need for pistols now.

***Smith** is agitated and keeps looking around.*

Chorus 3 Though Smith can see nothing uneasy anywhere in the white landscape, he cannot rid himself of the feeling that they are being watched, closely.

Mr Mansfield What is it, Smith?

Smith Nothing. Just the cold.

Chorus 1 The house at Prickler's Hill.

*The **Chorus** exit. **Smith** and **Mr Mansfield** arrive at the house. **Andrews**, an old footman, enters, stage left. **Mr Mansfield** offers **Andrews** his visiting card.*

Andrews Yes, yes, of course, sir. I should have known you. You have been here before.

Mr Mansfield Long ago.

Andrews Long ago, sir.

***Andrews** indicates with his hand.*

Andrews There used to be grand paintings hanging on these walls.

Mr Mansfield I remember them... I remember King Saul and David.

Andrews Aye, sir. That was the first to go.

Mr Mansfield To go?

Andrews Sold. Sold, sir, to pay the butcher, the baker, and...

Smith (*Interrupting*) And the chimney sweep down the road.

Andrews If you will, lad. The chimney sweep down the road – whoever he may be!

Smith A gent with a wooden leg.

***Andrews** looks at Smith with dislike.*

Mr Mansfield Is Mr Lennard here?

Andrews He's in Barnet, though we do expect him back here by midday.

Mr Mansfield Good! Our difficult journey won't have been in vain, in that case.

Andrews Miss Field, the deceased's sister, and two of the nephews are here. The others are with Mr Lennard, sir. They are always with Mr Lennard. They give him no peace, sir – not even to conduct the business. He stayed here, sir, for two nights. But he had to leave. They were at him all the while. You'll not find a cushion, chair covering nor bolster that hasn't been slit, nor a floor board unopened. The family have been hard at it. They have a heathenish belief that the master hid a great fortune somewhere against the chance of poor dead Jack's returning! But Jack will come back when his father does – and that will be at the judgement of us all! Not a day before!

Smith *(To Mr Mansfield)* We'd best ask Andrews where Jack played as a boy.

Mr Mansfield *(Sharply)* Why? D'you still have your hopes? If so, forget them Smith. We'll wait for Mr Lennard. This is his affair alone.

***Miss Field** enters. She is a gaunt-boned elderly lady. She carries with her a cushion that has been slit open and throughout the conversation she searches through its stuffing.*

Miss Field Mr Mansfield! Kate Field at your service, sir! Sad times, Mr Mansfield! A brother dead... The family penniless! – Oh! A sad life, my brother's, a tragedy, Mr Mansfield. Never, never for a day did he get over the loss of Jack. Always expected him to come riding up the drive. Not a worthy son! Not likeable. Though I was his aunt, I say it – and God forgive me – he's better off dead! I mean – for there they lie in the churchyard; my brother with his dear wife. Maybe he's with his precious Jack in heaven now. And maybe he repents of having hid his fortune away from us. You come at a sad time, sir! And all on account of the money! Oh, where can it be? God knows we've searched. *(She begins to exit)* Do forgive me, sir. Serve wine, Andrews! Excuse me, Mr Mansfield. I must go for there's still work to be done.

*The preoccupied **Miss Field** exits.*

Smith *(To Mr Mansfield)* Ask him!

Andrews It's twelve years now and still they've not forgiven Jack for being loved! Still they dislike him – abuse him – hate and envy him – as if he will indeed come riding up the drive and snatch some trifle out of their hands.

Mr Mansfield Is it twelve years already, Andrews?

Andrews Twelve years ago it was, and Jack had just been twenty, with the world before him. And then – he vanished. Gone into London it was supposed, and been swallowed up. There was a tale he'd been pressed* aboard a ship that had gone down with all hands off the Lizard*. He's dead now, so why can't they let him and his name rest in peace with his father?

***Andrews** starts to exit.*

Smith Mister Andrews!

***Andrews** pauses and turns.*

Smith Tell us, what was Jack like as... as a boy?

Mr Mansfield *(To Smith in an undertone)* Smith!

Andrews Why he was well-built – very well-built. Handsome. Oh, yes! And thoughtful. He was of a thoughtful disposition.

Smith Were he like me, then?

Andrews *(Sneeringly)* He was – country bred!

Smith D'you mean he didn't run an' climb an' play like... like other lads. Didn't he 'ave no favourite places to nip into when the going was 'ot; didn't he have any little alley or court he could call his own, Mister Andrews?

Mr Mansfield *(Fiercely)* Smith!

Smith For if he didn't, Mister Andrews, he weren't a very natural boy!

Andrews Where you, boy, might make a nest in the dirty corner of the wicked town, Jack, when the secret mood was on him would go...

Smith Where? Where would he go?

Mr Mansfield Smith!

***Andrews** points beyond the house, stage right.*

Andrews There was Jack's nest!

*The **Chorus** enter carrying a statue of a black angel. They put it down stage right, to mark a grave. Then they watch the action.*

Andrews In yonder churchyard – by the statue of a carved black angel! There he'd sit and dream his dreams and, maybe, even watch us all. If you can just wait here, Mr Mansfield, sir, I will go and get the refreshments.

***Andrews** turns and leaves the stage.*

Mr Mansfield *(Whispering urgently)* Smith!

***Smith** moves slowly and silently towards the area, centre stage.*

Mr Mansfield Where are you? Smith!

***Smith** hides amongst the set.*

Chorus 1 There is just the silence and darkness. The boy has gone!

*In haste **Mr Mansfield** feels his way around the area stage left.*

Mr Mansfield Smith! Smith! Come back! You're mad, child! No one will help you now, Smith!

Chorus 2 Mr Mansfield feels cool air from an open door blowing on his face.

***Mr Mansfield** tries to find his way out of the house.*

Mr Mansfield Oh no, surely you're not foolish enough to go wandering into the graveyard! Come back! You'll damn yourself! Smith!

Chorus 1 No answer – nothing but the restless motion of the cold air through unseen shrubs.

__Mr Mansfield__ begins to make his way towards the area, centre stage. He calls out to Smith. __Smith__ comes out of his hiding place and starts to move towards the statue of the black angel. Suddenly, he stops and looks down.

Chorus 2 Smith sees certain recent footprints in the snow. Footprints that frighten him. Footprints that freeze him, body and soul.

Mr Mansfield Smith! Come back!

Although he is preoccupied by the discovery of the footprints, __Smith__ hears Mr Mansfield's voice and turns to see him wandering about the area, centre stage. __Smith__ moves towards Mr Mansfield, and takes hold of his hand.

Mr Mansfield Smith?

Smith Quiet! Someone's been here already!

Mr Mansfield Child...

Smith Quiet, I tell you!

Carefully __Smith__ guides __Mr Mansfield__ towards the churchyard.

Mr Mansfield Where are you dragging me, child?

Smith To the churchyard.

Mr Mansfield Why?

Smith You'll see.

Mr Mansfield Have you forgotten – I'm blind?

Smith Not that blind, Mister Mansfield.

Chorus 2 Down, down to the churchyard – with the snow flurrying secretly about them – hurry the boy and the blind man.

__Smith__ reacts as though he sees someone coming. He pulls __Mr Mansfield__ into a hiding place, stage right. They are just visible to the audience. __Mr Black__ enters. He limps over to the statue of the black angel and sits down. Unseen by the others, __Andrews__ enters from the back of the stage and hides.

Smith He's there, by the statue! Old Hop-an'-Scrape! Whispering Jack! Jack o' the alley! Little Jackie Field – and the spitting image of his done-for Pa! It's my Mister Black!

Mr Mansfield The son! Mr Field's son? Alive!

Smith Yes, more's the pity! It was him what had the old man done in. Whispering Jack!

Mr Mansfield That is terrible!

Smith He's not of your opinion! For he's smiling!

Chorus 1 Who'd have thought the Devil was born in green fields out Barnet way?

Smith He's waiting for someone.

Chorus 2 Now they both know – beyond all doubt – the secret that Mr Field sought to take with him to his grave.

Chorus 3 Mr Field had discovered that his son, Jack, was still alive.

Chorus 1 Jack Field, a one-legged man, sitting in the shadow of an angel, waiting.

Mr Mansfield Jack Field, the hope of his father, a monstrous morsel of a man, who would be better off dead. What a discovery poor Mr Field made!

Chorus 2 Who can it be that is coming to meet with the Devil?

Smith Shhh! Someone is coming. Here he comes!

Mr Billing *enters and moves towards Mr Black.*

Smith Your friend and mine!

Mr Billing *(Calling quietly)* Jack!

Mr Black Billing!

On hearing the name of Mr Billing, ***Mr Mansfield*** *rises slightly.* ***Smith*** *pulls him back down.*

Mr Billing *(Urgently)* Have you got the document?

Mr Black No. Our friends in brown haven't yet come.

Mr Billing Well, it won't be long now, dear Jack.

Mr Billing *puts a hand on Mr Black's shoulder.* ***Mr Black*** *shivers visibly.*

Mr Black As you say, not long, dear Billing, and we'll be rid of each other.

Mr Billing Why, Jack! We're friends! Have been for years. Why the bitterness – now?

Mr Black You made me kill him, Billing!

Mr Billing You didn't do the deed!

Mr Black It's always felt as though I did! And you made me!

Mr Billing *removes his hand from Mr Black's shoulder.*

Mr Billing I made you? Jack, it's not so.

Mr Black You planned! You urged! You tempted! I blame you!

Mr Billing Ah, but you acted, Jack! Never forget that!

Mr Black How can I forget? Not till I die! And maybe not even then. You even swore it would be Andrews coming. You swore to me that it would be Andrews!

__Andrews__ has seen and heard enough. He exits quietly, unnoticed.

Mr Billing A murder's a murder, Jack – no matter who perishes. It's not you or me, Jack. It's this world we live in, Jack! What can we do? We've got to live. Take the rough with the smooth, Jack. It'll all come out in the wash! If there's a God in heaven, he knows the difficulties we're up against down here. He'll understand. He'll forgive us. And if there is no such Judge – well, Jack, what have we got to lose? It's all in the mind, my dear! Well, well – we'd all like to be saints through and through. Nothing nicer. But we can't. It's the world, Jack, not us. And we can't change that.

Mr Mansfield *(To himself quietly)* Oh, God for Judgement!

Chorus 1 What sort of Judgement can there be?

The two __men in brown__ enter and approach Mr Black and Mr Billing. __Andrews__ enters from the back of the stage. He carries a gun and, unseen by anyone on stage, he hides.

Mr Black *(Standing)* At last! Here come our men in brown. You took your time! The document! Hand it over, and quick about it!

Man in Brown 1 Sorry, but we've not got it!

Mr Billing Not got it! Why not? You've not killed the blind man, then? You let him get away?

Mr Black Fools!

*In rage **Mr Black** makes to hit one of the **men in brown**, but **Mr Billing** stays his hand, forcing it down to point at the snow.*

Mr Billing Look! There!

Chorus 1 What is it that Mr Billing finds so remarkable in the snow?

Chorus 2 Footprints!

Chorus 3 His own, the men in brown's the one-legged man's and two sets more – not to be accounted for!

Mr Billing Footprints! A large set and a small set!

*The eyes of **Mr Black**, the **men in brown** and **Mr Billing** follow the track of the footprints in the snow.*

Smith *(Whispers)* They've found us! We ain't got a chance, Mister Mansfield. Judgement's come all right – but it's come for us!

*The two **men in brown** begin to follow the footprints in the snow made by Mr Mansfield and Smith. They reach the place where **Smith** and **Mr Mansfield** are hiding. They grin and stop.*

Man in Brown 1 You think you can hide?

Man in Brown 2 Why not step out so that we can see you properly.

Smith They've found us! We ain't got a chance, Mister Mansfield.

Mr Mansfield For God's sake, go, Smith!

Mr Billing *(Screaming)* Kill them! No help for it! You've got to do it!

*The two **men in brown** take out short glimmering knives.*

Chorus 2 Agile Smith, quick as lightning Smith, could escape if he wanted to!

Chorus 1 Mr Mansfield would not reach the gate to the graveyard without a knife in his back.

Chorus 3 Smith, with all his wit, quickness, and fear, is not capable of leaving the blind man behind.

Mr Black Deal with them.

Man in Brown 1 That's what we intend to do.

Lord Tom *enters and points his pistol at the two men in brown.*

Lord Tom Stop. Hold. Stand there!

The two ***men in brown*** *stop and turn to Lord Tom.* ***Smith*** *and* ***Mr Mansfield*** *rise from their hiding place.*

Man in Brown 2 You dirty great bag of wind! Be off with you!

Lord Tom Spare the boy! I'll not have him harmed!

Man in Brown 1 You'll not? And who's you, Lord piddling Tom? Be off – or we'll slit you in tiny pieces, friend!

Lord Tom Smut! Never fear! Lord Tom's beside you! I'll save you! I'll blow blue daylight through them.

Smith Be off, Lord Tom. You'd best save your own lousy skin! I'm done with you now! I know you and I don't like what I know.

Lord Tom *continues to point his pistol at the men in brown. He shouts at them.*

Lord Tom Keep back! Back!

Mr Black *takes out his pistol and holds it at the ready.*

Man in Brown 2 And if we don't?

Lord Tom Then you're dead as mutton!

__Man in Brown 1__ advances on Smith and Mr Mansfield. __Mr Billing__ exits quietly. __Lord Tom__ fires his pistol at Man in Brown 1.

Lord Tom Blue daylight!

__Man in Brown 1__ falls to the ground. __Mr Black__ fires at __Lord Tom,__ and wounds him. Even so, __Lord Tom__ remains standing and points his pistol at __Man in Brown 2,__ who runs off stage.

Lord Tom Blue daylight, eh, lad!

__Lord Tom__ sinks to his knees. __Mr Black__ realizes that he has been deserted and starts to exit. He passes close to where __Andrews__ is hiding. __Andrews__ waits until __Mr Black__ has passed him before calling out.

Andrews Jack! Jack Field!

__Mr Black__ stops and turns. __Andrews__ steps forward, lifts his gun and aims at Mr Black.

Mr Black The name's Black. Mr Black.

Andrews You are Jack Field!

Mr Black *(In mock surprise)* Why, it's Andrews, isn't it?

Andrews Don't move!

Mr Black How are you these days, Andrews? *(Pause)* Andrews, put down the gun. Come, man, do as I ask! Put down the gun!

__Andrews__ continues to point his gun at Mr Black.

Andrews You went away from Prickler's Hill! You killed your own father! You destroyed Mr Field! You should have stayed dead to us!

Mr Black Andrews, you don't understand these things. *(In fear)* Andrews! Don't do it, Andrews!

***Andrews** fires the gun. **Mr Black** falls dead. **Smith** leads **Mr Mansfield** to the injured Lord Tom. They both crouch down by the dying highwayman.*

Lord Tom *(To Mr Mansfield)* Glad to make your acquaintance, sir! Never... never thought to... shake hands, it's an honour...

Mr Mansfield And for me, Lord Tom. And for me!

***Smith** guides **Mr Mansfield's** hand to meet and grasp **Lord Tom's**.*

Lord Tom *(Whispering)* Nights on the Common, Smut! Duval... Turpin... Robinson... and... and...

Smith And Lord Tom!

***Lord Tom** dies. **Smith** starts to cry.*

Chorus 2 Smith and Mr Mansfield wait with Lord Tom and Andrews stands on a hillock, above the fallen figure of Mr Black, whose real name was Jack Field.

Chorus 1 Mr Billing, who had corrupted Jack Field, is nowhere to be seen.

***Miss Field** and **Mr Lennard** enter. **Mr Lennard** moves to **Mr Mansfield** and helps him to his feet.*

Chorus 2 Mr Lennard, the lawyer, returns to Prickler's Hill and is informed of events and discoveries.

Chorus 3 Miss Mansfield arrives on foot from a nearby village where Mr Billing had insisted she stay while he was at Mr Field's house at Prickler's Hill, as though to spare her from the tragic news he was confident that the men in brown would tell him – that her father had been murdered on Finchley Common.

Miss Mansfield *enters. She moves to her father.*

Mr Mansfield *(To Mr Lennard and referring to Smith)* My guardian angel, sir. A little singed and tattered about the wings, but then he's flown through the caves of hell! Meet Smith.

Mr Lennard *(Stiffly)* Pleased to meet you, I'm sure.

Smith *bends close to the body of Lord Tom.*

Smith Lord Tom! You blew blue daylight through 'em just like you said!

Smith *stands up.* ***Miss Mansfield*** *moves to him and puts her arms around him.* ***Footmen*** *enter and remove* ***Lord Tom, Mr Black****, and* ***Man in Brown 1****.*

Smith *(To Miss Mansfield)* I'm sorry about Mr Billing, miss.

Mr Mansfield Smith, what did Lord Tom look like?

Smith 'E was a big man, Mister Mansfield, and always wore green. Green 'at, green cloak, green breeches, and bright green eyes as well. 'E was a real, gallant, high toby, Mister Mansfield. One of the best!

Mr Mansfield He... went well, Smith.

Smith None better, Mister Mansfield.

Mr Mansfield He's in heaven, Smith.

Smith If there's a Common up there, that's where 'e is, Mister Mansfield. Right up 'igh on the snaffling lay!

Mr Mansfield *takes out the document and gives it to* ***Mr Lennard*** *who opens and reads it.* ***Smith*** *moves away from the others and stands alone, speaking to himself.*

Smith Bleeding mail-boy, that's what I been! Documents took and delivered. No charge. And you may 'ave confidence. I'll rent me an office in the shadow of St Paul's. Come wind, come snow, come Newgate jail and the death of friends – Smith gets through with the documents. From Curtis Court to Prickler's Hill in less than three months. Well done, Smith!

Chorus 1 With Mr Field's document read, a sexton* is sent for.

*The **sexton** enters carrying a spade. He starts to 'dig' beneath the black angel.*

Chorus 2 The sexton digs beneath the black and peaceful angel.

***Mr Mansfield** and **Miss Mansfield** move towards Smith.*

Mr Mansfield Come, Smith. Let us see it out.

***Mr** and **Miss Mansfield** together with **Smith** join the others who are watching the **sexton** dig. Suddenly, he stops digging.*

Sexton Ah! What 'ave we 'ere? *(Pause)* No nothing! A slab of stone. Sorry good people.

Chorus 3 Had Mr Field hidden nothing?

Sexton (*Continuing to dig*) Ah! What's this? Something here not buried by me. Let's see... a wooden box... a travelling box...

*The **sexton** places a travelling box, from the set, beside the black angel.*

Miss Field It was his! I know it! He always used to take it with him to...

Sexton (*Interrupting*) But he's left it behind now, ma'am!

Miss Field Open it.

*The **sexton** uses his spade to 'strike off the strap'. He opens the box. Apart from Smith, everyone moves towards the travelling box. The **Chorus** move towards Smith.*

Chorus 1 Mr Field's box is filled, stuffed with a prosperous lifetime of guineas! Guineas upon guineas lie in sunny shoals, gleaming and winking in the cold light.

Smith There must be at least a hundred thousand gold flatties in the box - a hundred thousand!

Blackout.

Scene 10

Lights up. The area stage right is set as the cellar of the Red Lion Tavern. ***Miss Bridget*** *and* ***Miss Fanny*** *are sitting on stools, sewing old clothes. The* ***Chorus*** *are present on the edge of the area.*

Chorus 1 The cellar of the Red Lion Tavern - Miss Fanny and Miss Bridget are sewing mournfully.

Chorus 2 Miss Fanny having heard of the death of her admirer Lord Tom, is red-eyed and sniffy.

Chorus 3 Miss Bridget does not speak, but sits and sighs and from time to time shrugs her shoulders.

***Smith** and **Mr Mansfield** enter. **Smith** guides **Mr Mansfield** towards the steps of the cellar of the Red Lion Tavern.*

Miss Fanny It's him!

Miss Bridget Never!

***Smith** comes down the steps, misses his footing and falls with a clatter. **Miss Fanny** drops her sewing and gets to her feet.*

Miss Fanny It's him. It's Smut.

Miss Bridget And about time, too! Oh, you felonious child! We thought you was shamefully dead!

***Smith** picks himself up from the floor.*

Smith Dead? What business would I 'ave being dead with ten thousand guineas to me name? Answer me that!

***Miss Fanny** puts her arms around Smith overjoyed at the news. **Miss Bridget** shakes her head in disbelief. **Smith** steps away from Miss Fanny and in a grand manner and with much bowing, fitting for his new status, he addresses Miss Bridget.*

Smith Sister Bridget. How do you fancy a carriage and pair, and an 'ouse in Golden Square?

***Miss Bridget** smiles, nods, and reaches out to ruffle Smith's hair.*

Miss Bridget *(As though joining in the game)* I'd say, I'd like it very much. When do we move?

Smith Tomorrow. And what would you say to a footman, a maid and a coachie?

Miss Bridget I'd say very elegant, child. When do we engage them?

Smith Tomorrow.

Miss Fanny Oh, Smut! You are good! Might we have a tall coachman, in green livery?

Smith *replies with a casual nod.*

Smith And what would you say to me offering me old friend, Mister Magistrate Mansfield, of Vine Street, a tot of what might warm him against the cold night air?

Miss Bridget I'd say it would be an honour and we'd be very pleased to oblige. When do we invite him?

Smith Now! Come in, Mister Mansfield! Prepared 'em! Mind how you go!

Smith *moves to help* ***Mr Mansfield*** *down the steps.*

Mr Mansfield Good evening, ladies. I've heard much about you...

Miss Bridget, *overcome by the importance of the visitor, hurriedly tidies the cellar.*

Miss Bridget Oh, Smut! You should have said – you should have warned – oh, Smut!

Smith Don't fret, Miss Bridget. He's as blind as a mole. If it wasn't for the whiff, he might as well be in St James's Palace! Ain't that so, Mister Mansfield?

Smith *takes an extra stool from the set and guides* ***Mr Mansfield*** *to sit on it. He then stands beside the blind man.* ***Miss Bridget*** *and* ***Miss Fanny*** *sit back on their stools and listen to Mr Mansfield.*

Chorus 2 Smith of the courts and alleys; Smith of the corners and byways and many a passing pocket.

Chorus 3 Smith, the ten thousand guinea man!

Mr Mansfield It is all true. Mr Lennard, the lawyer, while at Prickler's Hill, and with the beneficiaries' approval, awarded Smith one tenth of the churchyard treasure as a mark of gratitude and esteem. The sum of ten thousand guineas.

Miss Fanny I always said, Brid, that there was some good in our document, didn't I?

Miss Bridget *smiles at her sister.*

Mr Mansfield And what are you going to do with it, Smith?

Chorus 1 Smith does not reply.

Chorus 2 For despite his independence of pocket and his desire to go up in the world, Smith knows that as a truly free spirit, his affections must guide him.

Smith For my sisters, a shop in Golden Square. Miss Bridget and Miss Fanny - court dressmakers.

Miss Bridget. *(Overcome)* Oh Smut, what a good boy you are.

Miss Fanny *jumps up and hugs* ***Smith****.*

Miss Fanny And you, my fine gentleman, what will you do?

Smith Mister Mansfield.

Smith *helps* ***Mr Mansfield*** *up from his stool.*

Mr Mansfield Yes, Smith.

Smith It's getting late. It's time we both went home to Vine Street. We'll be missed.

Smith *takes* ***Mr Mansfield's*** *arm to guide him. Blackout.*

Activities

About the Author

Leon Garfield was born in 1921. He studied art before serving in the British army in the medical corps during World War II. After the war, he worked as a hospital laboratory technician before becoming a full-time writer – 'I seemed to drift into writing for children; or rather, I drifted into the sort of writing I like – which can have wildly exciting adventures and something of character and morality.'

Leon Garfield's historical novels made him famous as a children's writer. His stories are full of true historical facts which give the reader a real feel for the period. He took great time and care over the research for novels like **Smith** – 'Many of my discoveries about the period came from voluminous reading of diaries and letters to find out such things as the cost of a journey from Weymouth to London, the price of slaves, the situation of the law courts. I discovered all sorts of fascinating trifles, many of which were unusable.'

Leon Garfield lived in Highgate in North London with his wife, the novelist, Vivien Alcock, and he used London as the setting for much of his writing. His books have won many important prizes and have been translated into dozens of languages. Several of his novels have also been made into films and television adaptations (including **Smith**). Before his death in 1996, he worked on the award-winning Animated Shakespeare series.

Now Read On
Compare this play with the novel, **Smith**, on which it is based. You might also like to try other novels by Leon Garfield. Here is a selection:
- *Jack Holborn*
- *Devil in the Fog*
- *Mr Corbett's Ghost*
- *Black Jack*
- *The Strange Affair of Adelaide Harris*

These are all published by Puffin.

To find out more about life in the Eighteenth century, ask your librarian to recommend some history books. You could also look at old maps of London. Here are some suggestions for further reading about highwaymen:
- *Discovering Highwaymen* by Russell Ash (Shire Publications)
- *The Crimson Book of Highwaymen* by Peter Newark (Jupiter Books)
- *The Beggar's Opera* – a play about the highwayman, Macheath, by John Gay

For a typical romantic view of highwaymen read Alfred Noyes' poem, 'The Highwayman'.

Smith's World

Read

Smith's London

Smith is set in mid eighteenth-century London. This London was a very different place to the London of modern times. It was a lot smaller and surrounded by rural land, heaths and commons. There were many old wooden buildings in London, although the area around St Paul's Cathedral was fairly new as it had been rebuilt following the Great Fire of London in 1666. There was little development south of the River Thames and suburbs of modern London such as Highgate were then still villages.

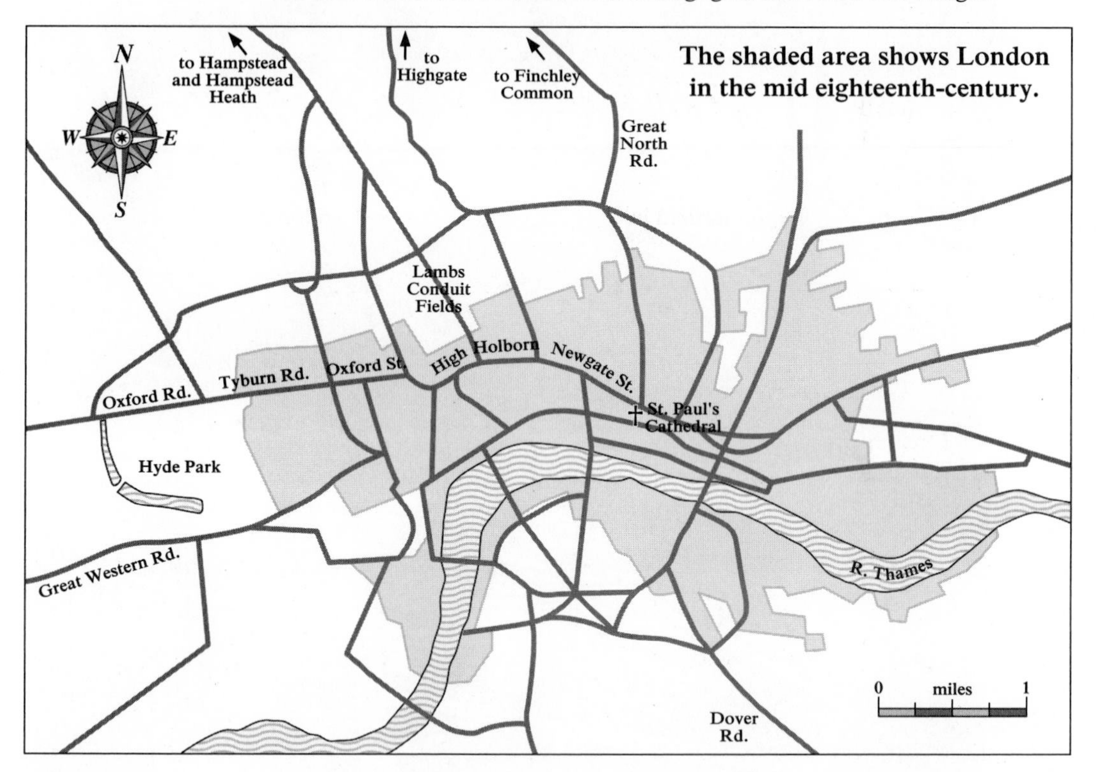

List and Search

Look back at the playscript and make a list of some of the places and street names that are mentioned. Try to find these on the overview map of eighteenth-century London on this page and the more detailed street maps on pages 108–109.

Research

Look at some maps of modern day London (you could try both a street map and a map that covers the whole of London). Compare these with the maps on pages 107–109. Are there any streets, places, etc. that still exist today?

Central London in 1746

Rocque's Map of London, 1746

Research and Write

Life in the Eighteenth Century

1 Divide into small groups. Each group has responsibility for collecting information about life in the Eighteenth century in Britain. Divide the following areas up between each group:
- travel and transport
- at home
- at work
- society
- architecture
- shops and markets
- crime and punishment
- literature and art
- life in the country
- life in the city

2 Each group has to research one of these areas and deliver a report back to the rest of the class in one or more of the following ways:
- as a talk
- as a written report
- as a 'Then and Now' wall display, using maps, pictures, charts, photocopies and written captions
- as a role play (you could have interviews with eighteenth-century characters, etc)
- as a radio programme (record this on a cassette tape)
- as a TV news programme (record this on video tape).

Read

Literacy

Smith A document! What use is that to me? I can't read! Not a word!

In the Eighteenth century, it would have been unusual for a boy like Smith to be able to read. In the London parish of Islington, between 1767 and 1814, about 75 per cent of children were illiterate.

There was no compulsory education and very few children went to school. Male children of the aristocracy and the rich merchant classes might have attended public schools like Eton, Westminster and Harrow. There were also grammar schools for boys from middle class families.

For females, it was a different story. In the Eighteenth century girls were not considered important enough to educate! It was a widespread belief that the only decent career for a woman was marriage. Consequently, there were very few schools for girls. Those fortunate to receive any formal education at a school, or at home with a private tutor, were taught subjects that would help them become 'good wives'. These included: sewing, dancing, singing, writing letters, and etiquette.

Charity schools existed for the education of the poor, but these were few and far between and standards were not very high. There was even a fierce debate amongst the ruling classes as to whether the poor should be educated at all. As one opponent of education argued: 'Does it necessarily follow that the lower classes will become more industrious, more virtuous, more happy by learning how to read?'

Smith Learn me to read!
Prisoner 1 Not in a thousand years my boy! Be happy that you can't. For what will you get by it?… Be advised, don't learn to read.

List

1 Look back at the playscript and make a list of what the different characters say about reading and writing. (Look at Scenes 1, 2, 4, and 5.)

Discuss

2 Using this evidence, discuss with the rest of the class the following points:
- Why do some of the characters refuse to teach Smith to read?
- Why does Miss Mansfield think it her duty to teach Smith to read?
- Does learning to read improve Smith's life?

Research and Write

Try to find out more about education in the Eighteenth century. Research and then write an encyclopedia entry for a CD Rom for one or more of the following subjects:
- public schools
- charity and Sunday schools
- dame schools
- education for girls
- universities

Crime and Punishment

Chorus 3 There's the hanging if he gets caught. Hanging! And that's for trying to stay alive.
Smith Oh, it's all right for the rich with money and houses and things. They don't need to steal.

Read

Poverty and wealth lived side by side in eighteenth-century London. Crime was rife (many of the poor were forced into criminal activity) and punishments were harsh. Both men and women convicted of murder and robbery could expect to be hanged, or at the very least, transported to the colony of Virginia in America. Convicted children under the age of seven could not be hanged, and those aged between seven and fourteen usually escaped execution. However, there were cases of youngsters who were hanged for committing murder. This is the punishment Smith would have faced if he had been brought to trial and found guilty of murdering Mr Field.

Read

Newgate Prison

Newgate was England's main prison for over 700 years. It was a notorious place where prisoners waited for trial, execution, deportation to the American colonies, or for a reprieve. Debtors and their families (some spent many years in prison, unable to pay off their debts) lived side by side with murderers and hardened criminals.

Newgate was a place of filth and disease. Many prisoners died in the overcrowded rooms. The supply of drinking water came from a well that had sewage running into it. Typhus was common and known as 'jail fever'. The worst recorded case of jail fever at Newgate happened in 1750. A hundred prisoners on trial spread an infection that killed four judges and forty members of the jury and court officials. After this, all Newgate prisoners had to be washed from head to foot in vinegar to purify them before they could go out in public.

Today, the Central Criminal Court (The Old Bailey) stands on the site of the old Newgate prison.

THE CONDEMNED CELL IN NEWGATE.

Read and List

Re-read Scene 5 and then work out a time-line of the events which take place during Smith's imprisonment in Newgate. Do this as a calendar by recording what happens on each particular day. Start your time-line on the day Smith is imprisoned and end it on the day he escapes.

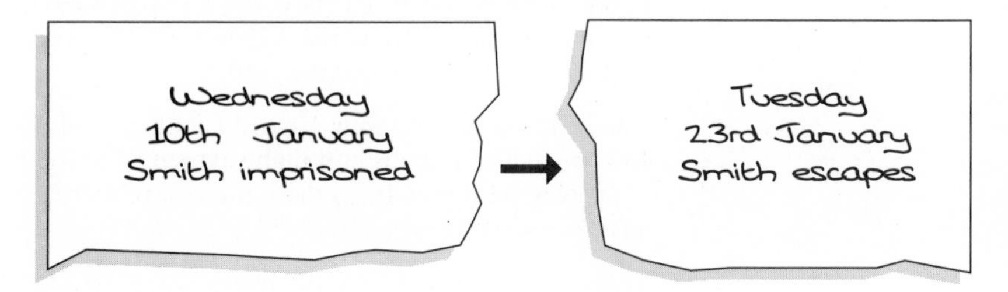

Include the following events:

- Mr Billing's visits
- escape plan hatched
- date for Smith's trial
- Meg's visits
- Miss Mansfield's visit
- Smith's sisters' visits
- Dick Mulrone's execution
- Mr Mansfield's house broken into by the men in brown.

Read

Highwaymen

Four main highways led into London in the Eighteenth century:

- the Great Western Road (now the A4) passing through Hounslow Heath
- the Great North Road (now the A1) passing over Finchley Common
- the Dover Road (now the A2) passing Shooter's Hill
- the Oxford Road (now the A40).

The heaths and commons around London were dangerous places, crawling with footpads and highwaymen. With no professional police force to protect the public from these thieves, robberies were commonplace and travellers were always at risk.

Instead of being despised, the highwayman had the respect and admiration of the public. He was seen as a 'gentleman thief'; being polite to his gentleman victims and gallant to the ladies – a better class of criminal than the common thief or footpad. The highwayman was a romantic figure; someone who lived dangerously, a person only one slip up away from being hanged at Tyburn. He was the stuff that legends are made of.

Dick Turpin is arguably the most famous highwayman of all. His legend centres on his famous ride to York on his horse, Black Bess. In fact, like most stories surrounding highwaymen, it was made up. A nineteenth-century writer of historical novels, called Harrison Ainsworth, invented most of Turpin's exploits. In reality, Turpin, like most highwaymen of his time, was a common criminal who cared little for his victims. He never owned a horse called Black Bess, let alone rode it to York.

Read and Discuss

In small groups re-read Scenes 3 and 6. Discuss the following points:

- What kind of image of the highwayman is suggested by Lord Tom?
- What is Miss Bridget's view of the life of highwaymen?
- Which view do you think is nearer the truth?

Read and Draw

Design a wanted poster for Lord Tom which includes the following information:

- his description
- why he is wanted
- what the reward money will be.

You can find some of this information in the playscript. Look especially at Scenes 3 and 9 and the list of characters on page 4.

Read

Tyburn

Tyburn was situated where Marble Arch is today. Executions had been held there since Norman times. Between 1749 and 1771, more than 250 highwaymen and hundreds of other criminals were executed at Tyburn.

'The Idle Apprentice' by William Hogarth

The hanging day at Tyburn was known as Tyburn Fair. A hanging day was a public holiday and thousands of people turned out for the executions. When the famous thief, Jack Shepherd, was hanged in 1724, 200,000 people attended his execution. Grandstand seats were sold to those people who wanted to get a good view of the hangings. These cost as much as two shillings and sixpence in 1758 – the equivalent of about £8 in 1997. (See A Note on Money on page 127.)

The journey from Newgate prison to Tyburn was only three miles in distance, but took over three hours to complete. The condemned highwayman would put on a show of bravado, play up to the crowd, and stop and have a last drink at an inn on the way, before mounting the gallows and delivering a final speech.

Once he had been hanged, carrier pigeons were released to take the news back to Newgate. For many highwaymen, the punishment didn't stop at their death. Their bodies were placed in gibbets (iron cages) or hung with chains and placed on wooden poles near where they had committed their crimes as a deterrent to others.

Read

Read All About it!

The Eighteenth century saw a great rise in the newspaper industry. The first newspaper to be published on six days a week was the *Daily Courant*. This first appeared in 1702. By the mid-eighteenth century, there were dozens of newspapers being printed on a daily basis.

Some of these newspapers helped to create the legend of the romantic highwayman. Like today's tabloid newspapers they sensationalized news and paid for exclusive stories. Daniel Defoe, the author of *Robinson Crusoe*, worked for a newspaper called *Applebee's Gazette*. He managed to persuade condemned highwaymen to tell him their story before they were executed. He would then sell copies of this at Tyburn as the criminal was hanged, thus achieving a red hot, world exclusive. Some of the condemned even advertised the fact that their story was available to buy as part of their final speech! Of course, these stories were often exaggerated and romanticized in order to make the criminal appear more than just a common thief.

Research and Write

1. Imagine you are a reporter for a tabloid newspaper. Find out more about the following famous highwaymen of the Seventeenth and Eighteenth centuries:
   - Dick Turpin (1705–1739)
   - Claude Duval (1643–1670)
   - Jack Shepherd (1702–1724)
   - James Maclaine (1724–1750)
2. Write up their story as a report for your newspaper. Consider the following things:
   - What is your view of the highwayman?
   - How will you get people to buy your paper?
3. Now write an entry on your chosen highwayman for an encyclopedia or CD Rom. How does the way you write about the highwayman change?

Read

Gin

It is surprising for a modern audience to read that a twelve-year-boy like Smith could buy and drink gin; however, in eighteenth-century society, this was a commonplace event.

Gin became a popular drink in the reign of George I (1714–27). Although ale houses had to be licensed, anyone could sell gin. In London, there were thousands of gin houses, especially in the poorer areas of the city. In these gin cellars, dozens of drunken people sat on straw, propped up against the wall, until the effects of the gin wore off and they could begin drinking again! The famous offer to customers was 'Drunk for a penny. Dead drunk for two pennies. Clean straw for nothing'. There was also no minimum age for buying or drinking the spirit.

However, the cheapness and the availability of the drink caused great social problems. Between 1721 and 1751, there were thousands of deaths caused by excessive gin drinking. In London in the 1740s, there were twice as many burials as baptisms. Children were left to fend for themselves and poverty and squalor were direct effects of the gin problem. The famous novelist, Henry Fielding, became a magistrate in 1748 and wrote: 'Gin is the principal sustenance (if it may be so called) of more than a hundred thousand People in the Metropolis. Many of these Wretches there are, who swallow Pints of this Poison within the twenty Four Hours; the dreadful Effects of which I have the misfortune every day to see, and to smell too.'

Crime was also a direct result of the addiction. It wasn't until the government tackled this in 1751, by passing a parliamentary act to curb the production of spirits, that the gin problem began to diminish.

Discuss

Below is a copy of Hogarth's *Gin Lane*, a famous engraving from the period. What does it tell you about Hogarth's view on the effects of gin on the local population?

Discuss

1 What sorts of reasons do people give for today's crime problems?
2 Can you see any similarities between the gin problem in eighteenth-century London and today's problems in society? Discuss these with other members of the class.

Characters

Talk and Write

Connections

There are many links between the characters in **Smith**.
Draw a diagram to show how the characters are connected. You may wish to make a large copy of this and display it on the classroom wall. This connections diagram has been started for you. Add the following characters:

- Andrews
- Miss Mansfield
- Miss Bridget
- Miss Fanny
- Mr Lennard

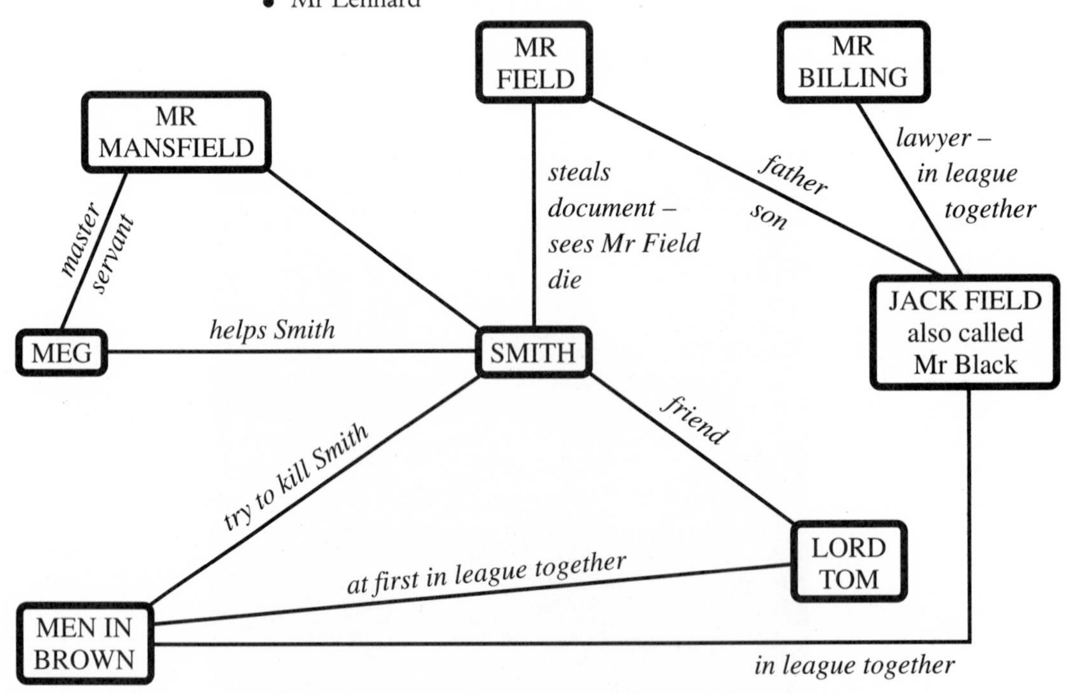

Talk and Write

Character Studies

1 Choose one of the following characters from the playscript:

- Smith
- Lord Tom
- Mr Mansfield
- Miss Mansfield
- Mr Billing
- Miss Bridget
- Miss Fanny

2 Make a list of words that describe them.

3 Then, look for examples in the playscript that back up the words you have chosen. For instance, if you think that Smith is kind, find an incident in the play that supports this viewpoint. You might find it helpful to record the information on a chart like the one below.

CHARACTER	DESCRIPTION	EVIDENCE
Smith	Kind	Scene 3 - He helps Mr Mansfield Scene 8 - He warns Mr Mansfield about the men in brown.

4 When you have finished this, share your findings with other members of the class.

Changes

During the course of the playscript, several characters have their lives changed by the events of the story.

Discuss

In pairs, discuss how the lives of the following characters change between the time we first meet them and the end of the play:

- Smith
- Mr Mansfield
- Miss Mansfield
- Lord Tom
- Mr Black

List

Choose one of the people above and make a detailed list of the differences between that character's life at the beginning of the play and at the end. For example, if you choose Smith you could begin your list like this:

CHARACTER	BEGINNING	END
Smith	Poor Lives in a cellar	Rich Lives in a house

Discuss

1 When you have made your list, get into small groups and share your ideas.

2 Discuss what events have caused these changes in each character's life.

3 Report back your ideas to the whole class.

Talk and Write

During the course of the play, characters also change their opinions of each other.

1 In small groups discuss how the following characters change their views of each other:
- Smith of Lord Tom
- Mr Mansfield of Smith
- Smith of Mr Mansfield
- Miss Mansfield of Smith

2 Then make a list of these changes of opinion and the events and reasons that lead the characters to make them.

3 You could do this as a hot seating exercise (see page 122) by choosing someone to play either Smith, Mr Mansfield, or Miss Mansfield and questioning them about how and why their views have changed.

Write

Before the Play Begins

1 Write an episode from an earlier time in Smith's life. Base your characterization of Smith on what we see of him in Scene 1 and what the Chorus tell us about him. You could use one of the following ideas as a starting point:
- a pickpocketing episode in which Smith nearly gets caught
- having to steal food
- an adventure with Lord Tom
- visiting a highwayman in Newgate
- attending the execution of a fellow thief at Tyburn.

You could write this in story form or as a playscript.

2 Write a ballad, a playscript, or a story about Lord Tom and his life as a highwayman.

3 What will happen to Smith now he is rich? Write a story about the events which take place after the play has ended. You may want to consider the following ideas:
- Will Mr Billing try and gain revenge?
- Will Miss Mansfield be happy about Smith living with her and her father?
- What will happen to Smith's sisters?

You could write this as a playscript or as a short story.

List

Dishonesty

Several characters are dishonest during the course of the play.

1 Make a list of the characters who lie to others and under what circumstances they do it.

2 Are they justified in lying? Back up your reasons with details from the playscript.

Discuss

1 Are there any wholly 'good' characters in Smith? Discuss your ideas with the rest of the class.

2 Does it get harder for Smith to lie to certain people during the course of the play? If so, who are these characters and why do you think this is?

Father and Son

Smith is an orphan – he doesn't have a father and no mention is ever made of him. However, Lord Tom and Mr Mansfield take on the role of a father figure to Smith.

Discuss

As a class, discuss the way that both Mr Mansfield and Lord Tom act towards Smith. Consider the following questions:

- Who is the best father figure in the play?
- How does Smith act towards Mr Mansfield and Lord Tom?
- How does this compare with the way Jack Field acts towards his father?

The Chorus

In this adaptation, Robert Staunton introduces a Chorus of three people. He says 'The Chorus are only visible to the audience and should be ignored by all the other characters in the playscript'.

Discuss

1 In small groups, answer the following questions:
- At what points in the playscript do the Chorus take an active role?
- What information does the Chorus give the audience?
- Why do you think Robert Staunton has a Chorus?
- Is the Chorus an effective device?

2 Share your ideas with the rest of the class.

Drama

You can use the following drama techniques to help you to explore the play further.

Improvisation
You are given a situation to work on in groups. Using your own words, you act out a scene which shows what you think about the subject. There are two main types of improvisation.

Planned: in this you are given time to prepare your work by talking with your friends and trying out your ideas. When you have practised your work and are satisfied with it, you show it to other people.

Instant: in this you are given a character and a situation, but you are not given any time to prepare. You must start the improvisation straight away.

Still Image
A still image is like a photograph. Any number of people may be in the image. A situation is chosen and the group must produce a frozen picture as if they had just been captured on film by a photographer or on canvas by a painter. You may wish to choose just one image or use a series of images to tell a story.

Thought Tapping
This helps us to understand what the characters in a still image are thinking. In turn, each member of the group says what their character was thinking at the moment the 'photograph' was taken.

Hot Seating
When a member of the group has played, or is about to play a character in an improvisation, a role play, or a written play, they can be put in the 'hot seat'. This means that other members of the group can ask them questions, and they must answer them **in the character** of their chosen person.

Hot Seating

Smith in Newgate

1. Imagine that Smith has just been thrown into Newgate prison. Prepare a list of questions to ask Smith as he sits in the cell. You can use the following questions as a starting point:
   - What are Smith's thoughts?
   - What can he do?
   - Is there anything he wishes he had not done?
   - What is his view of the other characters in the play at this moment in time?
2. Choose a member of the class to take the role of Smith and 'hot seat' them.
3. Now imagine that it is the end of the play. Prepare a different set of questions to ask Smith. You might want to include the following:
   - How has he changed?
   - Was it all worth while?

- What has he learnt from his experiences?
- Will he miss anything from his old life?
- What is he looking forward to most about his new life?

4 Choose another member of the class to take the role of Smith and 'hot seat' them.

5 Hot seat other characters from the play.

Life in a Debtors' Prison

Look at the following picture. It is a scene in a debtors' prison painted byWilliam Hogarth.

Still Image

1 In small groups, re-create this scene. Think about the following things:
- Who are these people?
- Why are they in prison?
- What is going to happen to them?

Thought Tapping

2 Now give each character a thought that they are thinking at the moment captured by the image. Show this still image to the rest of the class and speak out each character's thoughts.

Improvise

3 Use this image to spark off ideas for a rehearsed improvisation. The scene can be the starting point of the improvisation, the end, or can occur during the course of the piece.

Improvise

Waiting for the Trial
Imagine that you are in Newgate jail awaiting your trial. Work out a monologue in which you speak your fears and thoughts. You could do this in role as Smith or Dick Mulrone or invent your own character. Present this to the rest of the class.

Trust Games

Smith What's it like – being blind?
Mr Mansfield Dark, Smith. Very dark.

Pair Work

Mr Mansfield's blindness leads to his reliance on others. He has to place his trust in other people including Smith, a person who is a total stranger. In order to realize how difficult this can be, try some of the following trust exercises in which a person is temporarily deprived of their sight.

1. Work in pairs. One person is blindfolded or simply closes their eyes. The other has to direct the 'blind' student around the classroom or drama space (avoiding the other similarly 'blind' students) using only their voice. After a specific amount of time, swap over roles.
2. Repeat this exercise, except this time the 'blind' student can be led physically, by holding hands.
3. An obstacle course could be made with chairs, tables, rostra, etc. Students take it in turns to guide their 'blind' partner through the course by voice commands only.
   Extra tension can be created by timing how quickly each couple can complete the course without touching any of the obstacles.

Discuss

1. How did the 'blind' people feel during the exercise?
2. How did the people giving commands feel?
3. Which exercise felt most comfortable (voice only or physical guiding)? Why?
4. What happened when a competitive time element was introduced to the exercise?
5. If you were blind, with which of the guides below would you feel safest?
   - a teacher?
   - a friend?
   - a parent?
   - a brother or a sister?
   - a stranger?

This exercise could be extended by guiding a person around the school rather than within the confines of a single classroom.

Staging

If a play is described as being naturalistic, it means that what happens on the stage is just like real life – people act 'naturally', the set looks 'normal', and people generally speak to each other as they would in real life.

Talk and Write

Would you describe this adaptation of **Smith** as naturalistic?
If not, why not? Discuss this in small groups and make a list of your reasons.

Read and Design

Putting on the Play
Read A Note on the Set (page 6) and the stage directions that describe the settings. Using these, design a set for a production of **Smith** to take place at your school.

Design

Poster
Design a poster for a production of **Smith**. You will need to think about the following things:
- what information you wish to convey
- how to make the poster eye-catching
- what images you want to use.

Draw

Costumes
Design some costumes for the characters in the play. You will need to find out what style of clothing was worn in the Eighteenth century. You can research this in special costume history books or use pictures of the period in which **Smith** is set. The playscript will also give you information about what clothes the characters wear.

Research

Music
You could use music in a production of **Smith**. Try to listen to pieces of music written during the 1700s to use as backing music. Look out for:
- court music
- ballads and popular songs of the period
- the cries of street vendors

You should be able to find examples of these in your local audio library. Collections of contemporary ballads and songs of the period are available in book form or as sheet music. Again, your local library should be able to help you with this research. Alternatively, you could compose your own backing track in order to help create a dramatic atmosphere.

Glossary

Consumption	a physical condition characterized by a wasting away of the tissues of the body, especially as seen in tuberculosis of the lungs.
Needle through shoddy	'shoddy' is a yarn or fabric made from wool waste or clippings. It is a cheap material and is very easy to sew. Smith moved with speed as a needle would when passing through cheap material.
The Old Ditch	a narrow channel used for drainage. The Old Fleet Ditch in London ran North to South into the River Thames. (See the map on page 109.)
Lug	an ear.
High toby	a highwayman. A toby was a public highway frequented by highwaymen. A low toby was a minor road or bridle path.
Yardage of hemp	yardage is an amount or distance in yards. Hemp is a plant used for making rope. Smith is being warned that he will finish up being measured up for the hangman's rope.
Weevils	beetles that feed on plants and plant products.
Nubbed	executed by hanging.
Snaffling lay	to 'snaffle' is to steal. So Lord Tom has been waiting on the heath to hold up and steal from the passengers in passing coaches.
Smoked spectacles	spectacles with dark glass. Used by blind people.
Guinea	a gold coin worth 21 shillings coined in Britain between 1663 and 1813. Originally the gold was from Guinea. (See A Note on Money, page 127.)
Tyburn	near Marble Arch in London. Used for public executions by hanging.
Livery	a distinctive uniform worn by servants of a particular person or members of a city company.
Gibbet	a wooden structure resembling a gallows, from which the bodies of executed criminals hung. Also a gallows.

Come a–cooing	to 'coo' is to make a low, soft sound like a dove. The dove is a symbol of love. So Mr Billing has come to see and court Miss Mansfield.
Bedlam	St Mary of Bethlehem became a Royal foundation for lunatics in 1547. A lunatic asylum; a mad house.
Driblet of spittle	a small amount of saliva.
Turnkey	the keeper of the keys especially in a prison.
Footpad	a robber or highwayman on foot rather than horse.
Pressed	when a ship did not have a large enough crew, groups of seamen, known as press gangs, would force (press) ordinary men to join their ship to make up the numbers.
The Lizard	a rocky point south of Land's End in Cornwall.
Sexton	a person employed to act as caretaker of a church and its contents and graveyard. Often used to signify a gravedigger.

A Note on Money

Old money is not straightforward. In eighteenth-century England, people thought in terms of pounds, shillings and pence. There were twenty shillings in a pound and twelve old pennies in a shilling.

In 1971, the currency changed and where there used to be twenty shillings in a pound, there were now twenty five-pence pieces in a pound. However, this can be confusing because 1 shilling = 12 old pennies, but 1 new 5p piece = 5 new pennies.

The most important thing to remember is that a penny was worth a lot of money in Smith's London, and that two shillings and sixpence – the price of a seat at a Tyburn hanging – is equal to about eight pounds today.

Plays in this series include:

Across the Barricades — ISBN 0 19 831272 5
Joan Lingard adapted by David Ian Neville

The Bonny Pit Laddie — ISBN 0 19 831278 4
Frederick Grice adapted by David Spraggon Williams with Frank Green

The Burston School Strike — ISBN 0 19 831274 1
Roy Nevitt

The Canterbury Tales — ISBN 0 19 831293 8
Geoffrey Chaucer adapted by Martin Riley

Carrie's War — ISBN 0 19 831295 4
Nina Bawden adapted by Robert Staunton

The Demon Headmaster — ISBN 0 19 831270 9
Gillian Cross adapted by Adrian Flynn

Frankenstein — ISBN 0 19 831267 9
Mary Shelley adapted by Philip Pullman

Hot Cakes — ISBN 0 19 831273 3
Adrian Flynn

Jane Eyre — ISBN 0 19 831296 2
Charlotte Brontë adapted by Steve Barlow and Steve Skidmore

Johnny and the Dead — ISBN 0 19 831294 6
Terry Pratchett adapted by Stephen Briggs

Paper Tigers — ISBN 0 19 831268 7
Steve Barlow and Steve Skidmore

A Question of Courage — ISBN 0 19 831271 7
Marjorie Darke adapted by Bill Lucas and Brian Keaney

Smith — ISBN 0 19 831297 0
Leon Garfield adapted by Robert Staunton

A Tale of Two Cities — ISBN 0 19 831292 X
Charles Dickens adapted by Steve Barlow and Steve Skidmore

Tess of the D'Urbervilles — ISBN 0 19 831439 6
Thomas Hardy adapted by David Calcutt

The Turbulent Term of Tyke Tiler — ISBN 0 19 831269 5
adapted from her own novel by Gene Kemp